"I'm not ready to leave," Kade said

Tanya stared back at him defiantly. "If I say so, you'll have to go!" she declared, longing to take the superior look off his face.

"Are you firing me, Miss Hume?" he asked in a silky voice that somehow held a hint of warning. "Because then there wouldn't be much left of the business, I assure you."

Tanya's eyes sparked as she returned his fire. "You mean you'd take our business with you? Well, of all the low tricks!"

"Who said it was your business?" Kade asked acidly. "I take only what is mine. And three-quarters of this business is mine."

Tanya sat stunned as she digested the shock. "I don't believe you," she said in a low voice, full of uncertainty. "You told me I'd inherited the business. You said nothing about joint ownership."

OTHER

Harlequin Romances

by JANE CORRIE

1956—THE IMPOSSIBLE BOSS
2020—RAINBOW FOR MEGAN
2038—SINCLAIR TERRITORY
2053—GREEN PADDOCKS
2072—THE BAHAMIAN PIRATE
2087—DANGEROUS ALLIANCE
2098—RIMMER'S WAY
2159—RAFFERTY'S LEGACY
2167—PATTERSON'S ISLAND
2194—THE TEXAN RANCHER
2209—PEACOCK'S WALK
2257—THE ISLAND BRIDE
2285—CARIBBEAN COCKTAIL
2313—THE SPANISH UNCLE

Many of these titles are available at your local bookseller.

For a free catalogue listing all available Harlequin Romances,
send your name and address to:

HARLEQUIN READER SERVICE,
M.P.O. Box 707, Niagara Falls, N.Y. 14302
Canadian address: Stratford, Ontario, Canada N5A 6W2

Tasmanian Tangle

by

JANE CORRIE

Harlequin Books

TORONTO • LONDON • NEW YORK • AMSTERDAM
SYDNEY • HAMBURG • PARIS • STOCKHOLM

Original hardcover edition published in 1979
by Mills & Boon Limited

ISBN 0-373-02335-9

Harlequin edition published June 1980

CHAPTER ONE

TANYA HUME swept down the passage that led to the secretary's office. Her blonde head was held high, making her diminutive five feet four height appear at least two inches taller. Her lovely grey-green eyes had taken on a definite green sparkle as she entered the office, not bothering to knock. This time she had gone too far, she told herself as she walked over the vast airy office towards the desk and stood facing the cool, lovely-looking brunette who sat in isolated splendour at her desk.

Tanya's blazing green eyes met the cold blue ones of Melanie Black, who glanced up at her with a hint of impatience in her look. 'Would you mind telling me why you fired old Mr Davidson?' Tanya demanded without preamble.

Melanie's eyebrows lifted fastidiously as she answered laconically, 'Because he's old, and what's more important, because he can't do his job. Any more questions?' she added with a touch of insolence in her voice.

Tanya's eyes took on an extra glint at this. 'He can't do his job because he's doing Ted Broom's as well,' she answered coldly.

'The staff are expected to double up when someone's sick,' retorted Melanie sharply, adding cynically, 'He should have been replaced long ago. He has trouble managing his own job as it is.'

'Sick!' repeated Tanya scornfully, preferring to ignore Melanie's unfair comments on John Davidson's work. 'Ted Broom doesn't pull his weight when he does deign to put in an appearance. I don't know all that much about the business as yet, but even I've noticed that much.'

Melanie's cold blue eyes studied Tanya's golden complexion and her bright flushed cheeks. 'Yes,' she drawled softly. 'You don't know much about the business,' she repeated slowly, making Tanya's flush deepen at this criticism, for that was what it amounted to. It wasn't her fault that Kade Player, the autocratic manager of Orchard Farm, had always found a good reason as to why she shouldn't get too involved with what, after all was said and done, was her business. 'So why don't you leave the decisions to people who do know?' went on Melanie, taking full note of Tanya's discomfort. 'Now if you don't mind, I've some letters to get in the post this evening.'

Tanya refused to be sidetracked and stood her ground; the memory of John Davidson's face as he had savoured the news that he had been dismissed spurred her on. 'Well, you'll just have to reinstate him,' she said firmly. 'If anyone deserves the sack it's Ted Broom,' she added acidly, knowing full well that the young assistant accountant was a particular favourite of Melanie's. His sleek good looks and fawning behaviour towards Melanie had up till now guaranteed his position, but not at the cost of old John's job, Tanya thought grimly, not if she had anything to do with it!

This time it was Melanie who had lost some of her cool, and she glared at Tanya. 'I think you'd better make your comments to Kade, don't you?' she queried sweetly. 'He usually leaves that sort of thing to me, but as you're set on revoking my orders then you'll have to deal with him.'

'Very well,' replied Tanya stoutly, feeling a tiny tug of worry. Kade did not like his staff's decisions overruled, and Melanie had been with him for many years. If the rumours were right, then she was more than a secretary. At this thought Tanya swallowed. The thought hurt more than she cared to admit, for she loved Kade—had done ever since she could remember, but she was only one of a devoted following of females from the typists' department to the mailing office; they all sighed over the tall handsome man who ruled the business with an iron hand.

It was odd, Tanya thought as she left Melanie's office a few minutes later, after the secretary had told her with a glint in her frosty blue eyes that Kade would be in about ten that morning, and if she was still in the same mind then she should come back to see him, odd that she had known Kade long before Melanie had applied for the job of secretary to him, yet Melanie's words would hold far more sway than hers would. He would automatically back Melanie's decision, and Tanya would have a hard time proving that in this case Melanie was wrong—not only wrong, but unfair, and somehow she had to make him see that.

It was not as if she was bent on making trouble, she thought miserably, though she was sure that Kade would see it that way. Without even trying she had somehow alienated herself from his good books. Her presence had always seemed to irritate him and Tanya had never understood why.

One could almost say that it went back to when Tanya was only ten years old, and Kade had first come to Orchard Farms to manage the business for her father. Yet on the face of things this was ridiculous—for how could a ten-year-old child set up such a reaction? Particularly in someone she had taken a liking to. At this thought Tanya grimaced; liking was not quite the right word, crush was more the word. She had followed the handsome manager around the farm in those early days on her pony, taking great care not to get in the way of his work.

She would watch him inspecting the acres of fruit and listen to his authoritative voice issuing orders, and whenever those piercing blue eyes of his would rest on her she would give him a timid smile offering friendship, but her tentative approaches were smartly nipped in the bud. Although not very old, Tanya had felt this rebuff keenly, and it had hurt. It still hurt, she thought sadly, for after an absence of ten years when she had returned home after her mother's sudden death, she found that she was treated as a complete stranger. Such was his welcome, as if it was her fault that her mother and father had separated, and her mother had taken Tanya away with her.

It was not as if Tanya had not made spasmodic visits back to the Huon Valley where she was born—she had; her father had insisted upon this condition at the time of separation with his wife. Her mother, though, had never returned, and Tanya's visits were made at the agreed times and only for an allotted period, no more and no less.

Her mother's recent premature death at the early age of forty-one, resulting from a skiing accident on the slopes of the Austrian Alps, had precipitated Tanya's arrival back in Tasmania, only to find that her father had died of a coronary two days before her return.

Still suffering as she was from the effects of her mother's death, one more blow was hardly felt by the numbed Tanya whose grief was for her gay, lovely mother she so dreadfully missed.

That was six months ago, and Tanya had since learned that she had inherited her father's business. This she was told by a brusque Kade after the funeral, and he had said that he would indoctrinate her into the business side of affairs. She could then, he told her with an almost disinterested air, contribute towards the running of the farm.

As with his earlier treatment of her when she was still a child, this cold businesslike attitude towards her had hurt her, and she had tried to tell him that she had no wish to make any changes and that she would be grateful if he would carry on in the same capacity for her as he had done for her father.

His reaction to her timid request had somewhat shaken her, for he had given a grim smile and thanked her for her confidence in his abilities. It had sounded a little sarcastic to Tanya's sensitive ears, and she could have cried at his rather obvious misconstruction of all that she had said.

This had left her with a nasty suspicion that he had no intention of staying on once she was in full command of the aspects of the complicated retail business that she had inherited, but there was nothing that she could do about that, and she had had to steel herself against such an eventuality coming to pass in the not too distant future.

She had long since given up any hope of piercing through the wall of Kade's dislike and mistrust of her.

She did know that he had been extremely loyal to her father. She also knew that her father and his father had been school chums many years ago, and that Kade had chosen to work for her father rather than his own, who owned a vast chemical complex near Hobart, and would probably return there when he left the farm. As for the past, the fact remained that her mother and father had decided to part, and whatever had been the rights and wrongs that had led to the parting of the ways, Kade had sided with her father, that much was obvious, but as none of it had been Tanya's fault, she was at a loss to understand the reasoning behind his cool, distant treatment of her.

At five to ten, she left the invoice department where she was at present working, or to be more correct, observing the various methods of invoicing employed by the firm, and made her way back to the office section inhabited by the hierarchy. Melanie's office in the forefront acted as watchdog to protect the senior staff from any needless interruption in the course of their duties, but mainly to preserve her illustrious boss's privacy at all times.

Her curt nod on Tanya's entry and grim, 'He will see you now,' told Tanya that she had given Kade her own version of Tanya's interference in what was exclusively her domain.

Tanya's legs felt decidedly weak as she crossed the large office and knocked on the door at the end of the room. The imposing notice that read 'Kade Player. Manager' did nothing to ease her tension as she waited for the imperative summons to enter.

At Kade's curt 'Come in' Tanya opened the door and feeling Melanie's baleful eyes on her back she entered the office.

Kade sat at his large cluttered desk immersed in paper work, and after glancing up briefly at Tanya who stood in front of the desk mentally rehearsing her defence of Mr Davidson, told her to wait a minute while he finished reading the article he had been studying before her arrival.

He did not ask her to sit down, Tanya noticed with a pang of sorrow, although she supposed there was nothing to stop her doing so if she wished. However, she stood where she was and waited until he had finished perusing the article in a magazine that was holding his attention. It was a trade magazine, Tanya noticed, and it did occur to her that he could have carried on reading it after she had left, but that was Kade, and was his way of underlining the fact that she was taking up his valuable time. It ought to have infuriated her, but it didn't simply because she loved him, so she stood there looking at his dark head bent over the article, and at his strong lean fingers that held the magazine page as he turned it slowly over to the continuation of the article on the next page.

'I hear you've ordered Melanie to reinstate Mr Davidson,' he said suddenly, making Tanya jump as she thought he was still reading the article.

'I requested that she should revoke the decision to fire him,' she answered quietly, letting him know that she did no such thing, at least not like that.

'Might I ask why?' he requested in a silky voice, and Tanya swallowed painfully. He wasn't making it too easy for her to defend her action.

'Because it's unfair!' she burst out before her courage deserted her. 'I know he's old, but he can't be expected to do two jobs, not at his age, and that's what he's had to do.'

Kade's brilliant blue eyes left the print and stared up at Tanya. 'Precisely!' he commented witheringly.

Tanya was pretty certain what he was going to add to this cryptic remark, so she said it for him. 'I know the staff are supposed to double up when someone's sick,' she put in swiftly. 'But Mr Broom appears to have a delicate constitution. I don't think he's put in a full week's work since he's been here,' she added meaningly.

'Feeling the reins already, Miss Hume?' he queried sarcastically.

Tanya flushed under this rather unfair remark and miserably wished that she didn't love him quite so much. She wouldn't let anyone else talk to her like that, but he mesmerised her.

'Mr Davidson has been with the firm for thirty years,' she replied stiffly, unable to meet those piercing blue eyes still watching her closely. 'And I don't think he ought to be thrown out like that. In any case, it's my opinion that he does pull his weight—or at least he would if he wasn't bogged down with someone else's work.'

'Your opinion?' Kade's voice still held derision, and his eyes were narrowed as he surveyed her coolly, making Tanya feel like a worm on the end of a hook.

She looked away from him quickly. 'I know I've a lot to learn,' she said in a low voice, 'but I do feel strongly about this.' Her eyes had a pleading look in them as she turned to meet his again. 'Couldn't he be given another position? Or find someone else to help him until he's caught up with his work?' she asked softly.

Her heart fell as she saw the familiar hardening of his jaw at her plea, and she wondered what she would do if he ever smiled at her, for he never had, yet she knew he could smile and could be quite kind to others, but not to her.

Kade stood up, abruptly signalling the end of the interview, if it could be called that, and Tanya then had to stare up at his six-foot height as he towered over her. 'I'm making no promises,' he growled, 'but I'll look into it.'

Tanya had to be content with that, but it didn't look very hopeful at all, and his last shot didn't give her much confidence in the outcome either. 'In future, Miss Hume, you'll leave these decisions to my secretary. When you are fully capable of taking over the business then you can make your own decisions, but until then leave the running of the works in the hands of my staff, understand?' he growled.

Tanya nodded miserably and walked to the door; her hand was on the handle when he added softly, 'I take it you don't get on with Ted Broom.'

That was all he said, but Tanya knew what he meant. Ted Broom was the office Romeo and it was considered an honour to be asked out on a date with him, for these invitations were few and far between, particularly as he had an eye for the main chance and had spent weeks cultivating Melanie's attention. Tanya could have told him that she had spent her first few weeks at the farm's offices warding off his unwanted attentions, but even so, she had received the definite impression that he thought that she was playing hard to get and was certain of eventual success.

No doubt that bit of information would have surprised Kade, Tanya thought bitterly as she left his office and walked past Melanie's desk with her head held up high. Particularly as he obviously thought that Tanya was working off a grudge against him. She could even see the way Kade would look at things. Ted had overlooked her in some way and she was out to get even with him. Her mouth folded tightly on the thought. He'd rather see things that way than credit her with any kindness towards an old employee.

Her eyes were bright with unshed tears as she reached the outer door of the offices. What had she done to him to make him treat her like that? Why would he never give her a chance to even be friends with him?

Mistaking the reason for the look of distress in Tanya's lovely eyes, Melanie commented smugly, 'I told you not to bother, didn't I? You were lucky he consented to see you, particularly when he knew what it was about.'

Tanya did not bother to answer this triumphant jibe of Melanie's but swept out of the office. Oh, how she wished she did know all about the business! She'd fire Melanie for a start, just as she'd fired old Mr Davidson, and come to that she'd fire the manager too!

By the time she had reached the invoice section she had worked off most of her temper. She couldn't imagine Orchard Farm without Kade, he was Orchard Farm. Since his arrival the firm had gone to the top of the export market and their inland sales had rocketed to astronomical heights, and he was the wizard who had worked the miracle.

For the hundredth time she wondered why her father had not left him a share in the firm since he knew better than anyone Kade's worth in the business. To Tanya it had been one of the unexplained mysteries that she never hoped to unravel, since she was never likely to be in a position that justified her asking such a question, not when Kade was one side of a fence and she on the other. A fence deliberately erected by Kade, and one that she could never climb; it was too high and absolutely impregnable, like the man himself.

Four days later Tanya heard that her efforts to save Mr Davidson's job had been successful. It was old John himself who told her and his blue periwinkle eyes had gleamed in appreciation as he recounted the conversation he had had with Kade earlier that morning. 'Said he'd do some sorting out,' he said with a smile. 'And I've an idea one of our staff is due for a shock,' he added appreciatively.

Tanya wondered if this was Melanie, for the staff came under her jurisdiction, but John was not thinking of Melanie. 'It'll take more than good looks and a suave manner to get him out of this one,' he commented thoughtfully.

So it was Ted Broom who was up for the jump, Tanya thought, and she wondered how Melanie would take that. Not very well if she knew Melanie, but this fact did not worry Tanya. If Melanie had done her job properly and had not been swayed by flattery from the indolent Ted, she would have seen that John Davidson was overloaded and age had nothing to do with it.

Later that day Tanya was asked to collect the mail from the secretary's office. The message had come from a harassed Mrs Rodgers who was head of the invoice section, and requested with an apologetic smile. It was the end of the month and statements had to be out by the following day, and all hands were concentrating on this task. The mail went out at four each day, and as it was the invoice section that contributed the greater bulk of the post, all other post was directed there initially and then taken down to the post room for entry and despatch.

This request would not normally have caused Tanya any hesitation, she was only too willing to be of some use to whatever section's work she was observing, but under the present circumstances she would much rather have had the task allotted to someone else. Particularly as she had, in Melanie's eyes at least, scored a victory over her, and her appearance would be seen as a crowing action that would cause further infuriation.

She could hardly explain this to Mrs Rodgers, however, and she was forced to accept the small but extremely awkward errand, hoping that perhaps Melanie was tied up in some conference or other with another member of staff.

When Tanya opened the door of Melanie's office after giving a discreet tap, for it had occurred to her that Ted Broom might just be present and making an attempt to justify his imminent removal from the firm, she saw that her hopes had been fulfilled and that Melanie was not at her desk. The pile of mail lay in a wire tray on her desk, and Tanya hurried towards it, intent on collecting it with the greatest possible expediency and thus preventing a meeting with Melanie.

She was halfway across the room when Kade's office door opened and she heard him say harshly, 'I don't care if the fellow's got a weak chest. He could have a dozen kids and a widowed mother for all I care. I'll have no hangers-on in this firm, you should know that by now. Offer him an outside job if you're so keen on providing for his future, but if he does stay he'll have to pull his weight. You're slipping, Melanie, Davidson should never have been fired. I've had to apologise to him for what was an error of judgment on your part, and I don't like that, so see that it doesn't happen again!' he added warningly.

Tanya's only thought was to get out of that office as soon as possible, the post collection was of secondary importance now. She could possibly come back for it later, but she couldn't let Melanie know that she had overheard her receiving what amounted to a rocket from her employer.

She had just got to the door when Melanie's biting, 'What do you want?' came over the room to her and forced her to turn round, desperately trying to look as if she had just arrived.

'I came to collect the post,' Tanya said timidly, 'but as you were busy I thought I'd better come back,' she tacked on, hoping that Melanie would think that she had only looked in the office and not entered.

It was the way her embarrassed eyes refused to meet Melanie's that had given her away, she thought afterwards, as Melanie's biting retort proved. 'So you heard, did you? Well, I hope you're satisfied!' she said savagely.

Tanya did not know what to say; she could hardly point out that what Kade had said was nothing but the truth. Melanie had made an error of judgment, and but for Tanya she would have got away with it. That was the trouble, she thought miserably, no one else would have dared to challenge her authority on the matter. She was saved from thinking up an answer to her hinted accusation that she had caused trouble by Kade stamping out of his office and passing them without a glance at either of them.

The slam of the outside office door unleashed another onslaught from the chagrined Melanie. 'He's never spoken to me like that before,' she said furiously, and at Tanya's half-surprised look at her vehemence went on, 'And don't think those kind of tactics will make Kade look at you either. Oh, I've seen the way you look at him when you think no one is looking!'

Tanya's deep blush confirmed Melanie's accusation that she was in love with Kade, and she gave a triumphant smile at her discomfort. 'And the fact that you now own the farm won't make a bit of difference either,' she added spitefully. 'He had too much trouble with your mother to risk tangling with you.'

Tanya's blush was now replaced by a whitish tinge as she absorbed the shock that Melanie had just given her. 'Just what do you mean by that?' she whispered, as if robbed of the power of speech.

Melanie gave an offhand shrug as if the matter was of no consequence to her, but Tanya saw that she was thoroughly enjoying herself. 'Ask anyone,' she answered laconically. 'You'll find it's the truth. She pestered the life out of him. He had to take a horsewhip to her in the end to make her get the message that he just wasn't interested.'

Tanya's shocked gaze met Melanie's malicious one. 'I don't believe you,' she said, still in that hushed voice.

'Please yourself,' commented Melanie happily, 'but you'll find I'm right. He wouldn't still be here if he hadn't promised your father to watch out for you, but as soon as you're ready he'll be leaving you to it.' She walked back to her desk and placed a piece of letter-head into her machine, then sat down ready to start typing. 'And I for one,' she went on viciously, 'will welcome that day. He's got other business commitments besides fruit farming, you know, and it's about time he concentrated on them, so hurry up and learn the business, Miss Hume, and we'll all be happy.'

The word 'happy' seemed to reverberate round Tanya's head, as she left the offices and made her way through the works section, and out to her home that lay within five minutes' walk of the works.

If what Melanie had told her had been the truth, then she would never be happy again, she thought bewilderedly, as her still partially shocked gaze rested on a ranch-styled building a little ahead of her that was Kade's quarters, near enough to the main house to enable him to stroll over in the evenings to partake dinner with his boss, and far enough away to provide privacy for each if required. Not that he had ever taken dinner with Tanya; she had never asked him for the simple reason that she knew that he would refuse.

Her mother and Kade! Tanya still couldn't take it in. She didn't want to believe it, yet Melanie's spiteful outburst had had a nasty ring of truth in it. If it was a lie then it could be exposed at any time and she must have known that.

Tanya closed her eyes. Her head felt light, as if it didn't really belong to her. She wasn't really there at all, and not one of the horrible things Melanie had said were true. She must be dreaming. 'Please let it be a bad dream,' she whispered, 'don't let it be true.'

CHAPTER TWO

WHEN Tanya reached Orchard House, she went straight up to her room. Connie Dean, the middle-aged housekeeper, would at that time be in the kitchen supervising the dinner arrangements, and as fond as she was of Connie, she had no wish to run into her at that precise moment in time.

Connie must have known, she thought dully, as she closed her bedroom door behind her and sank down on to her bed with legs that suddenly refused to support her. Everyone must have known, she thought bitterly, everyone but her.

So many things were now becoming clearer to her; Kade's cool, offhand manner, his dislike of her, for it could not be called embarrassment, not with a man like Kade. But how very unfair of him to transfer his dislike of her mother to her daughter!

Her soft lips twisted at this thought. Was it dislike or disgust? A bit of both probably. She closed her eyes; it was disgusting! Her mother must have been years older than Kade, and to have thrown herself at him like that—Tanya's small hands clenched into fists; how could she face him now, knowing what she now knew? She couldn't! She simply couldn't!

Her anguished eyes fell on a large signed photograph of her mother on the dressing table opposite her. 'How could you!' she whispered to the image of the beautiful woman who had brought her into the world. Her eyes left the photograph and met her own reflection in the mirror of the dressing table. Yes, she was like her mother, the same white-blonde hair, the same winged eyebrows above the large eyes, only her mother's eyes had been dark blue, but that was really the only difference between them, to see one was to see the other, and Tanya had never before had cause to regret this likeness.

It had once been a source of pride to her, and she had basked in the shadow of her mother's beauty, for such was Drusilla Hume's personality that the lovely daughter by her side appeared to be a pale reflection of the mother.

If was from her mother that Tanya had learned how to accept a compliment gracefully and never let it go to her head. She had also been taught how to rebuff an unwanted suitor without giving offence, and there had been occasion enough to watch this practice being carried out. There had been no shortage of admirers no matter where they went, but they were all held at a distance.

Tanya had never had occasion to wonder why, or if she had given the matter some thought, she would have presumed that her mother had had one failure behind her in the marriage stakes, and had no intention of repeating it. Willing would-be suitors were allowed to escort them to various dinners or dances, but that was as far as it went, and Tanya's mother had kept as careful a watch on her daughter's escort's behaviour as she had on her own. There was time enough, she had often told Tanya, for her to settle down in marriage.

Tanya had never queried her mother's words, for she adored her, and whatever she said went without opposition. There were times when Tanya had sensed that she was unhappy, she could tell when these were by the sad pensive look that would come into her wide dark blue eyes as her thoughts lingered on the past, and Tanya had longed to comfort her but was at a loss to know how, for she had never spoken to her about the past; all she had ever said about that time was that it was better that she had left.

She shook her head wearily. It didn't make sense. She had thought she had known her mother well enough to be able to refute the malicious story that Melanie had told her, but had she? She thought of all the admirers who had dogged their footsteps during the years after they had left Orchard Farm, most of them presentable, for the rich circles Drusilla Hume had moved in excluded any gatecrashers. She thought of one particular man who had been the most persistent, Lloyd Warren, a cattle king from Oregon who had no intention of taking no for an answer, but her mother's death had finally extinguished this determined bid. Even in his grief in losing the woman that he had set his heart on capturing as his wife, he had offered Tanya a home, she was part of Drusilla and he wanted to look after her, such was his devotion to her mother. Tanya had hated having to refuse this kind offer, but even if she hadn't had anywhere else to go, she would not have accepted; it would have been a painful association for both of them, and would not have helped either of them to heal the deep wound left by the loss of the person they both loved.

Tanya swallowed on these thoughts as she recalled Lloyd's last words to her before she left Austria for Tasmania. 'Remember, honey, I'm always here if you want me,' and he had given her a card with his home

address on. 'That number will find me no matter where
I am, you just shout, and I'll be there.'

She saw again the tall chestnut-haired American, his
lean tanned features now tight in grief, and his brown
eyes that used to twinkle with amusement at some airy
quip of her mother's, now bleak with sorrow. Of all
her mother's admirers Lloyd was the one Tanya had
heartily wished success to. He was good-looking and
easy-going, yet one had a feeling that behind his lazy
good humour lay a sense of purpose, and where her
mother was concerned the purpose was quite clear, he
made no bones about it.

Yet her mother had been just as determined to hold
him at a distance as she had the others, and this had
puzzled Tanya. She swallowed painfully as she recalled
her feelings at that time—she hadn't known about Kade
and her mother then, things might have made more
sense if she had known. Lloyd was handsome, but there
was only one Kade; Lloyd's eyes were brown, Kade's
were a brilliant blue that went right through you.

The cascade of tears splashed on to her cheeks, but
she did not shake them away. How could Kade have
resisted her mother when other men vied for her attention? He was human, wasn't he? and he certainly
wasn't a monk, in fact he had a reputation of loving
and leaving those who dared to cross his path, indulging in an affair in an attempt to snare him. He had
never married, had he? She gulped. Had he loved her
mother? Was that why he hadn't married? As there was
only one Kade, so there had been only one Drusilla
Hume.

Her mother had had pride too, and Tanya simply
couldn't see her throwing herself at him as hinted by

Melanie. Her lips folded tightly together. Kade must have encouraged her, and then got tired of the game. The words, 'He had to take a horsewhip to her to make her see that he wasn't interested', then seared through her brain, and her teeth clenched together tightly. How dared he! And how could her lovely mother have allowed things to get to that state?

Tanya got up slowly from the bed; she had to go down and let Connie know that she was back. As for Kade Player, she hated him for the humiliation he had heaped upon her mother, and fervently wished that she could avenge her in some way, but she couldn't see how, since she had no intention of throwing herself into the fray and confronting him with her thoughts on the matter. She didn't think she could even bear to look at him, let alone be in the same room with him. One thing Melanie and she had in common right then was that the sooner she learned the business the happier they would all be. She wanted Kade out, and she wanted him out fast. The place wasn't big enough for the two of them, and she wasn't going anywhere!

Tanya went down to the homely sitting-room and settled herself in her favourite chair by the window. There was a magazine story that she had been perusing the evening before and had not finished, so she picked it up again and attempted to lose herself in the story. After a few moments she found her eyes could not concentrate on the print. It was becoming blurred— like her life, she thought wildly.

A heavy step outside the door made her hastily blink back the tears that threatened to gush out at any moment. She couldn't let Connie see her like this, she thought, and got up and stood looking out of the window with her back to the door.

The door opened and Connie entered. 'You're back early, aren't you?' she said, with a hint of surprise in her voice.

'Oh, I had a bit of a headache,' replied Tanya, desperately trying to keep her voice on an even keel.

'In that case I'll get you a cup of tea and a tablet,' replied Connie kindly, as she walked back to the door.

'Please don't bother!' Tanya's voice cracked on the last word, as if tea would solve her problems! She just wanted to be left alone.

She felt Connie's gaze rest on her bent head and prayed that she would let well alone until she was more in command of herself, but she ought to have known better. Connie had nursed her when she was a child and knew her too well to be fobbed off by the lame excuse of a headache.

'Like to tell me about it?' Connie asked gently, making the tears Tanya had held at bay escape and course down her cheeks.

'I can't!' was all Tanya could say. 'Leave it, Con, there's a pet. Perhaps later, but not now.'

'Been hearing things, have you?' asked Connie astutely, and Tanya turned to face her. Connie gave a deep sigh. 'I guess it had to come out some time,' she said slowly, and walked over to a chair opposite to where Tanya had been sitting. 'Sit down, Tanya,' she said gently, and sat down herself. 'Who told you?' she asked as Tanya's slight frame sunk into her chair.

Tanya's listless eyes met the sympathetic brown ones of Connie. 'Does it matter?' she asked miserably. 'It's true, isn't it?'

'It matters a great deal,' answered Connie firmly. 'There's ways of telling a story—the right way or the wrong way. It's my guess you heard the wrong version, am I right?' she demanded.

Tanya swallowed. 'I don't see that it does,' she replied dully, 'either way it's——' she closed her eyes. 'It's disgusting!' she got out, 'and I can't see how ...' she could get no further.

'And what's disgusting about it?' demanded Connie with a light in her eyes. 'Well, go on, tell me?'

Tanya couldn't meet her eyes, she looked away quickly then said in a low voice, 'She must have been much older than him, that's why!'

'Five years!' exclaimed Connie, in a matter-of-fact voice, then added firmly, 'You're forgetting the fact that your mother was only twenty when she had you, and that made her thirty years old when Kade first came to Orchard Farm, and Kade was twenty-five. Five years between them, that was all, so what's so disgusting about that?' She leaned towards the despondent Tanya. 'I don't know what you've heard or who told you, but I'd lay odds it was a woman, and a jealous one at that, am I right?' she queried persistently.

Tanya nodded wearily, and Connie went on firmly, 'Well, let me tell you how it really was. I won't have you blaming your mother for what was a nasty quirk of fate. I loved her,' at this point her eyes misted over. 'Some folk are born to happiness, others are not,' she said simply. 'Your mother never really stood a chance. If she'd been a plain girl then she might have stood a chance of some happiness, but she wasn't, she was a beauty with an ambitious father who ruled her with a rod of iron and picked out a rich husband for her when she was barely eighteen.' She gave a deep sigh. 'I remember her mother, your grandmother, she was a gentle, timid woman, but just as much under her husband's thumb as Drusilla was. It wouldn't have occurred to either of them to oppose his plans for his daughter's future, and to be honest I have a feeling Drusilla was only too glad to be given a chance to escape from her father's presence.'

At Tanya's half impatient shake of the head she went on firmly, 'You have to know how it was, otherwise you'll never understand any of it. She did try to make a go of the marriage, Tanya, and if it hadn't been for Kade——' she moved her plump hands in a vague gesture and drew her breath in sharply, 'but then I'm not sure, I know she was unhappy. It didn't take her long to find out that she had exchanged one kind of prison for another. Oh, your father was good to her, but he was too old for her, and set in his ways. He was forty-two when he married her and he adored her to the point of suffocation. He was a quiet man, too, and they really had nothing in common, except you, and you were the reason I believe she stayed as long as she did.

'I'm not trying to whitewash the whole thing or trying to find excuses for her, I'm just trying to make you see how it was.' She gave another sigh. 'But that's exactly what I'm doing, isn't it? Finding excuses for her, but there she was, not living in the true sense of the word but just existing from one dreary day to another. Your father wasn't one for social occasions, and she couldn't very well attend them on her own, and he ought to have thought of things like that, but he didn't.'

Her hands moved restlessly in her lap. 'So along

comes Kade,' she said softly. 'A younger man than he is now, of course, but just as dynamic and just as attractive to the opposite sex. I think Drusilla saw him as the ideal man, like any other girl she had her dreams, dreams that in her case had never been fulfilled, and in Kade she saw the sort of man she might have married.' She gave a whimsical smile at this point. 'Imagine how she felt, Tanya, as sheltered a life as she had led, she suddenly found that her beauty was ignored, and no matter how she tried Kade continually kept her at a distance.'

Tanya swallowed. She didn't have to imagine, she knew, she had received exactly the same treatment from him.

'So before she knew it she had imagined herself head over heels in love with him,' resumed Connie, unaware of Tanya's thoughts. 'She used to think up little gambits to give her an excuse to go and find him on the farm. She made it her business to know where he would be at a certain time and just casually drop by,' at this Tanya gave a painful wince, and Connie's sympathetic eyes met hers. 'She wasn't herself, Tanya. It was a kind of madness that had possessed her, and I don't think anyone could have done anything about it except Kade, and he did.'

'He took a horsewhip to her, didn't he?' whispered Tanya, who felt that she had heard enough, and was beginning to feel sick.

Connie's eyes blazed for a moment before she said harshly, 'She didn't spare you much, did she? I know now who told you. It was Melanie Black, wasn't it?' she demanded, and before Tanya could answer she went on, 'That particular story isn't general property, and she didn't get it from Kade either. That little besom has a way of ferreting out information, particularly if it concerns Kade, but it didn't happen that way,' she told Tanya, who now had her eyes closed and sat hunched in abject misery. 'I can tell you the true story, because Drusilla herself told me, and you're going to hear it, there's enough mischief been done without adding lies to it.' She went on quickly before Tanya could attempt to stop her as it was obvious that she wanted to.

'I told you how she used to seek Kade out, didn't I? Well, she'd gone to the stables this time, just as Kade was about to ride out on his rounds of inspection of the orchards. She was in riding kit herself and she probably hoped he would ask her to accompany him, but of course he did no such thing. Drusilla was so piqued that she completely let herself go, and slashed out at him with her riding whip. It was sheer frustration that made her act so out of character. Kade caught the whip and threatened to use it on her if she didn't leave him alone.' Connie gave a grim smile. 'I guess he didn't wrap it up, the time had come for plain talk, and you know Kade, he doesn't mince his words.' She sighed deeply. 'The trouble was, one of the employees who was looking for Kade heard that last part of it and cleared off to spread the news. Kade quickly put a stop to that, though, and the episode was completely wiped off the records.' She shrugged. 'But you know how folk are, they relish things like that, although no one would dare to repeat the story for fear of losing their job, not around here anyway.'

She gave Tanya a curious look. 'What did you do to infuriate her? She could lose her job, you know, if Kade finds out.'

Tanya's eyebrows lifted in surprise, 'Melanie lose

her job?' she repeated with a slightly sceptical air. 'I thought she was Kade's right hand.'

Connie gave a grim nod at this. 'So she may be, but anyone else could fill the same position given the years she's worked for him. She's not the only efficient secretary around, although she thinks she is. Well? You still haven't told me how she came to tell you something that ought to have remained buried in the past.'

Tanya pushed back a strand of her white-gold hair that had fallen across her forehead, with a weary gesture. She wanted to forget that part of it, but she never would; up until then her life had been full of expectation, now it was empty and echoed with bitter memories of the past. She was grateful to Connie for putting the record straight, not that it made things any easier for her, for in essence Melanie had told the truth.

Her wide grey-green eyes rested on Connie, but there was no light in them now, for they were haunted with sadness. Connie was waiting for an answer—she owed her that much at least, she thought. Tanya told her about how she had challenged Melanie's decision to fire Mr Davidson and how she had got him reinstated, ending tiredly with, 'I don't think she would have taken it so badly if I hadn't happened to be in the office and overheard Kade tearing a strip off her.' She shrugged her slim shoulders. 'I couldn't help overhearing, his office was open when I went into her office, and I wasn't able to get out fast enough.'

Connie nodded sagely. 'That must have hurt her pride,' she commented, with a certain amount of satisfaction in her voice. 'But it's about time someone stopped her gallop. I know for a fact that she's got rid of several of the old hands long before they were due to retire. It's been a case of you either get on with the secretary or you were out, she's gathered a nice bunch of cheer leaders around her as a result.' She nodded her head again. 'She's had it all her own way up to now, and it's gone to her head, but I wouldn't mind betting she's doing a bit of nail-biting now for ripping into you like that, she must be terrified that Kade will find out she's blabbed.'

Tanya's mouth set in a firm line. 'He won't find out from me,' she said grimly. 'The less I see of him the better. If he's such a good manager he ought to have known what was going on in the offices,' she added cryptically.

Connie gave her a surprised look, then pursed her lips in a disapproving way. 'He's a busy man, Tanya, as long as the work is carried out that's all he worries about.'

'Precisely!' Tanya bit out. 'The man's a machine! I doubt if he has any personal sentiments on anything.'

'Now you've no call to talk like that,' exclaimed Connie quickly. 'As for being a machine, you're not talking about the business, are you? It's my guess you're thinking of your mother!' At Tanya's quick glance away from her searching eyes, she continued, 'Would you have expected him to have an affair with his employer's wife? If you did, then you don't know Kade. Your father helped his father out years ago when a big holding of his stocks crashed. Your father stood surety for him, and he's never looked back from that day to this. He owns the largest chemical complex in the country now, but he would have been finished years ago if it hadn't been for your father. That's why Kade chose to work for him, he felt he owed a debt, and he respected him too much to indulge in any underhand affair, no matter what.'

Tanya's eyes searched Connie's honest ones. 'Do you think he loved my mother?' she asked her.

Connie shook her head firmly. 'No, pet, he didn't. She told me this herself, and it's a thing a woman usually knows, no matter how much they might try to fool themselves. Whatever Kade said to her that day, it pulled her round. I found her sobbing her heart out in the laundry room where she thought no one would find her. She told me she was ashamed of herself, she'd been a fool, and didn't think she could ever forgive herself for giving way to such madness. She must have made her mind up then to go away.' She gave Tanya a small smile. 'She had her pride, you know, and I guess she just couldn't live with it. Your father had probably guessed what was going on, but he must have known that he could rely on Kade's integrity, and he loved your mother enough to hope that things would settle down again,' she sighed. 'But it wasn't to be. Within a week she had left, and taken you with her.'

Tanya ate very little supper that evening. She hadn't been able to face dinner, and an understanding Connie had let her off without scolding her. She had very little sleep that night, her mind was too active. She felt desperately sorry for her mother who must have known so much unhappiness, and now she was able to understand why she had never remarried. She had made not one, but two bitter mistakes in the past, and was not likely to risk a third. As for Kade, Tanya's feelings remained the same. She felt that he could have put an end to the miserable situation much sooner than he had— or failing that, have left himself. If her father had been

given a choice in the matter he would surely have
wanted to keep his wife and child beside him, for
Tanya couldn't see how he could have remained ig-
norant of what was going on, although it was hardly
something that could be discussed openly without a
great deal of embarrassment on all sides, so in Tanya's
eyes it had been up to Kade to move out.

Her lips twisted wryly at this thought. Not Kade, she
thought, he was so used to women falling over him that
it would never occur to him that a woman had her pride
too. She could see only too well his reasoning on the
matter. If the woman had made a fool of herself over
him then he had no sympathy with her, and if the
woman was married, then the sooner she learnt that her
place with with her husband, the better. He would have
no other thoughts on the matter, and it would never
occur to him to feel pity for them. He was utterly ruthless and as hard as nails, and she wondered how she
could ever have imagined herself in love with him.

Before she fell asleep that night, Tanya promised
herself that before another six months had elapsed she
would take over the reins of the farm—and if that
wasn't possible, she would employ another manager to
help her run the business. The second probability
would suit her better, she decided drowsily; she
couldn't see herself undergoing training from Kade,
not now, and not ever!

CHAPTER THREE

THE following morning when Tanya sat down to breakfast there were violet smudges under her eyes, and when she refused the cooked breakfast that Connie placed before her and said that she only wanted a cup of coffee, Connie placed her plump hands on her waist and said sternly, 'It's no use dwelling on the past, Tanya. What's done is done, and no amount of wishful thinking will change things, you just remember that.'

Tanya nodded curtly at this kindly meant scolding, but it didn't alter her feelings one iota. She hated Kade for what he had done to her mother. There were ways of telling someone you weren't interested, and she ought to know, he had used the tactic on her when she was only a child, and was still using it, but there was no possibility now of her making a fool of herself over him. 'Melanie said Kade had other businesses to attend to, is that right?' she asked Connie.

Connie gave her a straight look before she answered, 'I guess so. He's a business man when all is said and done. I did hear he'd bought up several fruit farms the other side of the valley—why?' she asked abruptly.

Tanya gave an off-hand shrug, 'Oh, he did say something about my running the business later on,' she said. 'I gathered he's got plans to move on, and of course there's his father's business too, isn't there?' Her brooding eyes rested speculatingly on the coffee jug.

'And you can't wait for that to happen,' remarked

Connie shrewdly. 'Well, I wouldn't count on it. Sure Kade's got other interests, but it's here that he spends most of his time. He could have got out years ago if he'd a mind to. It's also true that his father wants him back in the family business, but it's what Kade wants that matters.'

'Oh, yes,' replied Tanya cuttingly, 'I've learnt that much by now.'

'Off on a crusade to avenge your mother, are you?' demanded Connie.

Tanya's eyes were wide as she stared back at Connie and the hurt that was mirrored in them made Connie move quickly to her side and give her a slight hug. 'I told you how it was, pet,' she said, with a soothing note in her voice. 'And it was the truth. Don't take it out on Kade, for sure as sure, you'll regret it. He had a bad time, too, and you'd do well to remember that.'

Tanya stared down into the dark liquid depths of her coffee and gave Connie a weary half-nod, but said nothing, and Connie gave her another hug. 'Leave well alone, pet, and let the future take care of itself. You're home now, and that's all that matters.'

It was all very well Connie saying that she should let well alone, Tanya thought, as she set off for the office that morning, but her world had been turned upside down and she didn't see how it would ever be set right again. She had been walking around wearing rose-tinted spectacles, but now they had been taken away from her and had left her blinking in the harsh sunlight. It would take some time for her to adjust herself to this new world of brutal fact that she had been thrown into.

For the first time since she had arrived back at home

and started work in the offices, she was grateful for the fact that Kade had made certain of her keeping out of his way by assigning her work in the outer offices of the firm. He was not likely to seek her out on any occasion, and in the light of her awakening she was hardly likely to seek him out.

She sat next to a girl who was handling export slips and tried to listen to what she was telling her about the procedure carried out at this particular juncture of sales, but her mind would wander off on its own channels of thought and they had nothing to do with the intricacies of the export trade.

When Mrs Rodgers told her that Mr Kade wanted to see her in his office, Tanya's first reaction was one of panic. She didn't want to see him, it was too soon, she needed time to adjust herself before she faced him, but it appeared she wasn't going to be given that time.

As she walked through the corridors of the outer offices and through to the main section, she wondered if he had found out about Melanie's indiscretion, but couldn't see how. She did not see Melanie confessing and throwing herself open to his wrath, particularly after what had happened the previous day. Perhaps he wanted to tell her he had decided to leave the firm? At this thought hope soared high in Tanya's heart. Oh, if only it was that, and that he would take Melanie with him. But he would, she was sure of it, just as sure as Melanie had been herself. It had been her manner towards Tanya, for she was too clever to risk upsetting someone she thought would be her employer in a few months' time, and her attitude towards Tanya had never been what might be termed as 'subservient'.

With this thought in mind, it was a little unnerving

to find that Melanie's attitude had undergone a drastic change since their last encounter. She actually smiled at Tanya, but there was an anxious look in her eyes and something else that Tanya thought might be a kind of pleading. It did look as if Kade had found out, she thought with another stab of panic, and it was all she could do to keep on walking towards the manager's office. She couldn't discuss it, she thought wildly, and if he tried——

'Good morning, Miss Hume,' Kade's smooth voice greeted her, as she closed the office door behind her and stood waiting to hear the dreaded subject mentioned.

'Good morning, Mr Player,' she answered warily, keeping near the door ready to make her exit at the slightest hint of a conversation ensuing.

'Well, come in,' he said irritably, 'and sit down, we've a lot to discuss.'

Tanya swallowed. Not if they were going to talk about the past they hadn't! She walked over to the chair placed opposite him and sat down slowly. It might be as well to get it over with, she thought wearily, as her smouldering eyes swept over the immaculately dressed man sitting in front of her. If he said one word out of place she'd fire him! She wasn't quite sure how you did fire someone but presumed one just said 'You're fired!' The thought gave her comfort and she found herself actually hoping that he would step out of line.

He had been looking at some notes on his desk and Tanya's eyes had followed his gaze, but when she glanced up at him again she found that he was studying her with narrowed eyes. 'Something on your mind?' he asked bluntly.

Tanya started, but made a quick recovery. 'I believe

it was you who asked to see me,' she replied coldly.

There was no doubt that her reply had given him food for thought, if not startled him, but with his hard features it was hard to tell. One thing was certain, she had never spoken to him like that before. She had been timid and desperately anxious to please him, but those days were gone, she thought with a kind of bitter release.

He raised an expressive eyebrow before he picked up the list that he had been studying, then he handed it to her. 'That's a list of the firms we deal with,' he said curtly. 'Their files are in the secretary's office. I want you to study them, from now on you'll be working at management level. I'm having a desk put in Miss Black's office for your use. Your first function will be to watch points, nothing else, got that?'

It was Tanya's eyebrows that rose this time; anyone would think that he was talking to an office girl! 'Very well,' she replied stiffly, 'but I would like to point out that if any more dismissals are on the agenda, I want to be consulted first.' Her determined eyes met the now blazing ones of Kade. 'You said something about my eventually running the business,' she reminded him relentlessly, 'and in that case I see no point in having to reinstate staff who had been dismissed after I take over.'

There was a glint in Kade's eye as he said, 'Got your eye on a manager, too, have you?'

If he thought he was frightening her by threatening to walk out, then he had a shock coming, Tanya thought grimly. She shrugged her shoulders lightly. 'I'm sure someone would prove suitable,' she answered quietly.

'Well, that's too bad,' he said harshly. 'When I'm

good and ready to leave, you can fill my position, but
that will not be for quite some time yet, I can promise
you.'

Tanya stared at him defiantly. 'If I say so, you'll have
to go!' she spat out at him, longing to take that
superior look off his face.

'Are you firing me, Miss Hume?' he asked, in a silky
voice that Tanya didn't care for at all, for it held a
hint of warning in it.

'I'd rather request your resignation,' she lied sweetly.

He drew in a deep breath, and she held herself rigid
in her seat because she had a feeling that he would like
to shake her until her teeth rattled. 'I've a damn good
mind to do just that,' he ground out furiously, his eyes
like chips of blue ice. 'You wouldn't be looking for
staff then, but a buyer for what's left of the business,
and that wouldn't be much, I assure you.'

Tanya's eyes turned pure green as she returned his
fire. 'You mean you'd take our business with you? Well,
of all the low tricks!' she fumed at him.

'Who said it was your business?' he queried acidly. 'I
take what's mine. Three quarters of this business is
mine.'

Her eyes opened to their full extent and she sat there
stunned while she digested the shock. 'I don't believe
you,' she said, in a low voice that was full of uncertainty, for Kade was not a man to bluff. She swallowed.
'If that's true, why didn't my father explain the position to me—and you, come to that,' she said accusingly.
'You told me that I'd inherited the business, you said
nothing about joint ownership.'

Kade drew in a deep breath again, and Tanya
noticed that his strong hands had clenched into fists,

hands that he'd like to slap her with, she thought. 'Because that was how your father thought things were,' he said grimly.

Tanya's eyes were full of her deductions on the last telling statement. Kade had bought him out behind his back, no wonder he'd not left the firm all those years ago! 'I see,' she said quietly, and stood up quickly, not being able to bear being in the same room with such a man. 'In that case, would you care to buy me out too?' she asked, trying to inject a sarcastic note into her voice, but it just came out as an ordinary question and much more effective, for it showed her distaste for the type of man she thought he was.

'Sit down,' he growled at her. 'We've a long session ahead, and you're going to listen whether you like it or not.'

Tanya's reaction to that was to make a dart for the door, but Kade beat her to it with an agility she would not have credited such a big man with. Her startled eyes watched as he turned the key in the lock, and stood towering over her. 'I said, sit down.' he repeated slowly, 'and stop looking at me as if I was last year's pin-up boy. You know, don't you?' he shot out at her suddenly.

Tanya looked away from those searching eyes of his, and closed hers. She wasn't going to discuss that, not now, All she wanted was to run as fast as she could away from the works, away from Kade. 'I don't know what you're talking about,' she said quickly, feigning surprise. 'I didn't know that you owned the business— or as good as,' she tacked on wildly, wanting to distract him, but it didn't work.

'I'm not talking about the business,' he rapped out, 'and you know it. I'd like to know how the devil you found out, though. Who told you?' he demanded.

Tanya shook her head wearily; she had really had enough. 'Does it matter?' she said in a low voice, then her voice was pitched on a note of sheer desperation. 'Please, I don't want to discuss it, not now, not ever. I meant it when I asked you to buy me out. There's nothing more to discuss.'

'I'm not buying you out, so you can forget that for a start,' replied Kade, but this time in a less harsh tone, and placing his hands on Tanya's slim shoulders he turned her round to face him. 'Do as I say, Tanya, go and sit down,' he commanded.

Tanya shied away from his touch as though he were a repellent insect, and Kade took full note of the fact and his jaw squared. As she did not have much choice in the matter she did as he asked and sat down again.

He had never called her by her christian name before, she thought numbly, and remembered bitterly how often she had wished he would. She wanted to spit out at him that she would rather he called her Miss Hume, but he'd do just what suited him whether she liked it or not.

Kade's eyes went over her slight figure and those wide eyes of hers that mirrored her thoughts so revealingly. 'You're like your mother,' he said thoughtfully, 'and yet not. Unless I miss my guess I'd say you were a fighter. You'd stay and see things through, not run away as she did.'

The hate Tanya felt for him was there in her eyes as she looked back at him. How dare he casually discuss her mother like that! She had been too good for the likes of him. 'I understand that she lost her reasoning for a while,' she bit back at him, and felt a spurt of satisfaction as she saw a tightening of his mouth. Yes, that had got through all right, she thought.

'You're not going to believe this, but I entirely agree with you,' he replied harshly. 'And it put me in a hell of a situation, but I guess you wouldn't see that side of it,' he added grimly, then shot a look at her under his dark forbidding brows. 'Do you know why I chose to work for your father?' he asked her abruptly.

Tanya looked away quickly. If she wasn't very careful he would gain a point here and she didn't intend to give an inch. She shrugged as if to say that that part of it did not concern her, and her eyes met the piercing blue ones of Kade as she answered sharply, 'Yes.'

His eyes narrowed at this. 'Learned an awful lot in a short time, haven't you? I'd swear you knew nothing this time yesterday—am I right?' he demanded.

Tanya gave him a warning look that clearly told him that she was not going to discuss that part of it, but she needn't have bothered.

'Okay!' he said curtly, 'so you don't want to talk about it, but you're going to have to. What you don't tell me I'll find out. A lot of trouble was taken to keep the lid on the past. It's finished, and should have stayed that way.' He gave Tanya an assessing stare. 'Just look at you,' he said grimly. 'You're as white as a sheet, and I'm pretty sure you're trembling all over, in spite of that brave front you're putting up. If I made a move towards you you'd scream the place down, wouldn't you?' he asked in an almost conversational way.

'I wouldn't advise you to try it,' warned Tanya, with flashing eyes, 'because you're right. I would scream the place down. I want nothing from you, Kade Player, except your resignation!'

'And that you're not going to get,' he drawled. 'As for making a play for you, you'd be disappointed on that score, too. I'm afraid I don't hanker after kids, and you've a lot of growing up to do.'

'Is that the sort of advice you gave my mother when you threatened her with the horsewhip?' retaliated Tanya, furious at the way he had deliberately misinterpreted her behaviour towards him and making it look as if it had been a ploy on her part to goad him into making a grab for her. She could feel the wetness gathering at the back of her eyes, but she wasn't going to give way to tears, not in front of this man. Connie had been right, you couldn't win against a man like Kade.

'So that came out too, did it?' he growled ominously, in a tone that spelt an awful lot of trouble for someone, and Tanya wondered if Melanie was shaking in her shoes the other side of the door. 'Well, I guess that narrows down the field,' he added pithily.

'Does it matter?' said Tanya, in a voice that spoke of her distaste for the whole subject. 'I had to know some time, didn't I? and I'm glad I know. There were lots of things I couldn't understand before,' her voice was not quite as steady as it had been because she was thinking of her mother, 'and if you don't mind I would rather we dropped the subject,' she added with as much dignity as she could muster.

His harsh, 'Very well,' took her by surprise and she almost blinked at him. 'But there's things you still don't know,' he went on in a flat unemotional voice, 'and it's time you did.'

Tanya drew in a deep breath; now that the emotional side of it was over she felt she could cope. She waited for him to go on.

'Well,' he began, taking a cigarette out of a silver case on his desk and lighting up with a matching lighter, then drew on the cigarette and exhaled the smoke slowly, 'you know why I came, and that means that you also know how your father came to my father's aid by backing him when a load of stocks crashed.' He gave Tanya a hard searching look and she had a feeling that he was trying to make her see things from his point of view, but it wouldn't work, she thought dully; if anything it would make things worse, not better.

'So how do you think I felt when your mother made a dead set at me?' he demanded softly.

Tanya couldn't meet his eyes but stared dully at the carpet at her feet.

'Hell! It's just as embarrassing for me as it is for you,' he exclaimed furiously. 'Just climb down from that high peak you've settled yourself on and try and see things as they were. Sure, your mother had a bad time of it. So did I, and I'll tell you this for what it's worth, even if I'd been tempted, I wouldn't have done anything about it, I would have cleared out there and then.' He frowned in recollection. 'Perhaps I ought to have done anyway, but I didn't; like your father I thought that she'd come to her senses.' He drew hard on his cigarette. 'Maybe I was too hard on her,' he said slowly, 'but I saw no other way of getting through to her, she was living in a pipe dream. I didn't think she'd take off like that, though, I thought she'd more courage than that, but she hadn't.' His free hand clenched into a fist. 'She not only ran, but took you with her. How do you think your father took that?' he shot out at Tanya.

'He thought as much of you as he did of her.'

He crushed his cigarette out with a vicious stab, revealing his thoughts on the matter. 'It took a while to bring him round after a blow like that,' he went on harshly. 'I didn't hide the fact that I'd had to speak to her, either, I owed him that much; besides, he wasn't a fool, he knew what was going on. I offered him my resignation then, in case my being here made it difficult for her return, but he wouldn't hear of it.' His gaze rested on an old print of the farm hanging on the wall opposite him. 'I guess he knew she wouldn't be back,' he added slowly. 'He knew her better than I did.'

Tanya said nothing but transferred her gaze to the floor again.

'I'm only outlining the facts for you to understand the following events,' he said harshly, 'and why I acted as I did. There was nothing underhand in my acquisition of part of the farm. They say there's no such thing as coincidence, but I've other thoughts on the matter. Your father also took a fall on the shares, and one just as bad as my father's. It happened just six months after you left, and I knew one thing for certain, and that was that if I'd passed that information on to him, he'd have wanted to sell the business and recoup what he could. He'd no heart for a fight back even if I'd offered to stand surety for him. By that time I was in sole charge of all business affairs, and all that was required of him was to countersign any cheques that needed signing.'

He did not miss Tanya's twisted smile, or the thoughts behind it.

'Oh, sure,' he said harshly. 'I could have been swindling him blind, but it just so happens that I'm a partner in my father's business and I could have bought

Orchard Farm any time I'd a mind to do so, particularly as your father had lost interest in the business—but
I didn't. I wasn't going to give him a chance to get out
and spend the rest of his time brooding on the past. He
needed an occupation and I made sure that he got one.
I covered the loss on the stocks with my own money,
and the only way I could do that was to buy my way
into the business.'

Tanya felt ashamed of herself. Instinctively she knew
that Kade was telling the truth, and she wished desperately that she could bring herself to say thank you for
his loyalty to her father, but the thought of her mother
and her unhappiness kept her silent.

'And that is why you were named as the sole inheritor
of Orchard Farm,' he said quietly. 'Your father had no
idea that I'd had to buy myself into the firm to keep it
solvent. It's also the reason why I'm staying on, quite
apart from the fact that I own the greater share of the
property. I promised your father that I would watch
over your interests and teach you the business. Whether
you like it or not, that's precisely what I'm going to do.'
He gave the startled Tanya an assessing look. 'I said
that I thought you were a fighter. Am I wrong? Are
you going to stick it out, or run for it as your mother
did?' he challenged her harshly.

Tanya felt the tears gathering again; she wanted to
shout out at him that she took after her mother, and
wanted nothing to do with Orchard Farm—not now
that it belonged to Kade. She still couldn't look at him
and badly wanted time to think things out. She had
never envisaged going away again; she was sick of the
constant travelling to various smart resorts where the
better endowed people spent their time, idling away

their lives on a constant round of so-called pleasure, and when she had been unhappy she had thought of Orchard Farm. It had been an anchor in the sea of constant travels, an anchor that would one day hold her fast to the place where she belonged. Her father had told her often enough that her home was there and would be always waiting for her.

She looked back at Kade, who sat there with that still but watchful look, and the unhappiness in her wide eyes said more than words could ever convey. 'I'm sorry,' she said in a low but firm voice. 'I meant it when I asked you to buy me out,' she gave a weary shrug of her slim shoulders. 'As you refuse—well, I shall just have to remain a shareholder.'

She flushed under Kade's hard scrutiny. He could think what he liked of her, she didn't care.

'Where will you run to?' he asked with an ironic note in his voice.

Tanya stared at her hands, her fingers now closely twisted together. 'I haven't thought that out yet,' she answered, and somehow managed to give him a tight smile. 'Don't worry, I'll make out. There are a lot of friends I could join for a while at least.'

'Who, for example?' queried Kade, still with that touch of irony in his voice.

It was none of his business, thought Tanya, surfacing from her well of misery to give him a look that said just that. 'Just friends,' she repeated stonily.

'You mean your mother's friends, don't you?' he demanded persistently.

'If you like!' bit back Tanya crossly, tired of the whole wretched business and willing an end to this miserable meeting.

'And then what?' Kade demanded harshly. 'Oh, I've seen the bills your father settled in the past for you both. I hardly think your income is going to live up to those standards.'

Tanya stared at him. What was he talking about? They had lived on her mother's money, hadn't they? Her father had not been a poor man, and he had left her a legacy—she caught her breath on a raw sob—but it hadn't been enough to pay for the life style they had acquired since leaving home. So that was why she had never married again, or sought a divorce.

On seeing her look of utter astonishment, Kade nodded significantly. 'It was one of the conditions of the separation,' he said harshly. 'You might as well hear the rest of it now. Your father agreed on a separation providing your mother never remarried. He was looking out for your future. He didn't intend you to find yourself lumbered with a stepfather you might not have got on with. He meant you to come back here where you belonged, but you can't bring yourself to even do that, can you? After all he did for you!' he pointed out savagely.

The tears Tanya had held back for so long now cascaded down her cheeks, and she turned her face away from her tormenter.

A large handkerchief was thrust into her hand, the knuckles of which were now wet where she had tried to stem the flow of tears. 'Try that one for size,' Kade said gruffly. 'Go on, get it out of your system. I guess you've had a pretty rough time of it since yesterday, and I haven't made things any easier for you, but you had to hear the whole of it.'

Tanya hastily mopped her face, then wondered

vaguely what to do with the handkerchief, she couldn't very well hand it back to him in that condition. She gulped, then took a deep breath, concentrating only on not giving way to her emotion. If she did as Kade suggested, she had a feeling that she would never stop crying once she had let herself go.

'Well, that's that,' said Kade in a resigned tone that Tanya somehow did not connect with the Kade she knew. 'I tried, but I've failed. I might have known how you'd react. It was the reason why I clamped down on the past. Sure, you'd have to know some time, but I figured there was plenty of time. There's ways of explaining things, and I sure as hell didn't intend you to be thrown head first into the mire of the past, not that there's anything murky about it. I told you the truth. Your mother might have been unhappy, but she took the wrong way out.'

He was silent for a moment or so after this, and Tanya, still desperately hanging on to her shattered aplomb, wondered if he would now allow her to leave.

'It gets into your blood, you know,' Kade continued in an almost conversational tone. 'Watching the yield each year, and assessing the crop, not to mention the sight of the blossom each spring.' He looked towards Tanya, now twisting his very damp handkerchief in her restless hands. 'Have you forgotten what it's like?' he asked her quietly, then gave a wry grin. 'I guess I ought to bring my father out here at that time. He might be able to understand why I prefer this life to the city life.'

Tanya drew in a deep breath. If he thought he was helping her by reawakening treasured memories, he was way out, he was making it worse for her. As if she had forgotten the acres of blossoms in the spring!

'Look at me, Tanya,' commanded Kade, and in spite of herself Tanya found herself complying with this order, but there was hostility in her damp eyes. 'Forget your pride. It is pride, isn't it?' he added softly. 'And it's not worth it. At heart you're still the kid that used to follow me round the orchards on a pony. If things had been different we'd probably have been a working partnership by now instead of facing each other like strangers across a table. I want to keep my promise to your father if you'll let me. Put the past behind you, it serves no purpose whatsoever in letting it rankle. This is what your father wanted for you. Now what do you say, are we partners?' he asked her abruptly.

Tanya's lips twisted bitterly. What wouldn't she have given to hear him ask that question a few days ago! 'We're not partners,' she managed to get out through lips that trembled, 'how can we be? You own the business, and I'm only a shareholder now.'

His eyes narrowed at this, and she sensed his change of mood towards her. He thought she was out for mercenary recompense and it must have sounded just like that, but she was beyond caring, she only wanted out.

'It needn't always be that way,' Kade replied quietly. 'A few years' hard work and you could become joint owner of the business. You could at least give it a try.'

It had taken a long time for Tanya to get the message that Kade was simply not going to take no for an answer. When the fact finally sunk through to her tired mind, she knew she would have to play for time without committing herself. 'I'll think about it,' she said wearily, and stood up quickly to show him that she had no intention of arguing about it.

'I want your answer now, Tanya,' he said with slow deliberation.

'I've given you one!' she cried, exasperated. 'But you won't accept it, will you? What more can I say?' she added with a touch of desperation in her voice.

'I won't accept it because you haven't given me the right one,' he replied gently yet firmly. 'Look, give it six months, and if you're still determined to sell out then I'll accept your decision. Is that too much to ask? It will also give you time to work out what you want to do if you do decide to leave. Well, what about it?' he urged persistently.

Tanya swallowed; on the face of things it sounded a very reasonable offer. She did need time to acclimatise herself to her new position, not to mention the traumatic events of the last few hours. At least he was offering her a breathing space, but she wouldn't need as long as six months. It was plain, however, that he would not hear of a shorter time limit. 'Very well,' she said stiffly, and turned towards the office door with a feeling of thankfulness that it was all over.

'Thank you,' replied Kade gravely, as he walked to the door and unlocked it for her. 'I know I can rely on you to keep your word,' he added meaningly, as she began to move out of the office.

The significance of his last words was not lost on her as she passed the now apprehensive Melanie who sat at her desk giving a good imitation of a frantically busy secretary, but Tanya was not fooled. She had a shrewd guess that Melanie had been hovering outside the office door in an attempt to listen in to the conversation. The bare fact that Kade had locked the door after Tanya's entrance ensured this.

Kade's words lingered in her mind as she went back to the invoicing department, smothering a longing to walk right out of the works, and indulge in a haze of misery. Under the circumstances, Kade wouldn't expect her to carry on as if nothing had happened, but Tanya badly needed an occupation to take her mind off her troubles. The busy hub of the invoicing section would provide just such a sanctuary. There were no personal issues there, just work and more work.

Her assumption that Kade would not expect her to keep on working was shortly proved wrong by a telephone message passed on to her by Mrs Rodgers, who came to find her as she was filling in an export form under the guidance of the cheerful girl Tanya had been assigned to work with in that section. 'Mr Player has just told me you'll be working in the main office block tomorrow,' she told Tanya, adding kindly, 'We shall be sorry to lose you.'

Tanya acknowledged the sincere compliment with a small smile, but her mind was very busy. She had a feeling that Kade was checking up on her, and wondered what he would have done if Mrs Rodgers had told him that she had not gone back to the section. He would have gone to find her, she thought with a flash of unwelcome insight. She had given her word and he intended that she should keep it.

She wondered what would happen if she packed her bags that night and walked out early the following morning. She could do; there was nothing to stop her, she had enough money to get her to Hobart. At this thought her fingers clenched round the pen she was holding, but as Kade had so baldly put it, 'What then?' She had no experience of work to fall back on. Her mother had seen to her education, she had been sent to a prohibitively expensive school in Switzerland, where she had received a good education but precious little else, since the young ladies who attended such an establishment were not expected to seek their own living afterwards.

Even if she found some kind of employment such as waiting at tables in a café, or serving in a shop, it would only be a matter of time before Kade tracked her down. He had accused her of having too much pride, but what about him? Wasn't it pride that had made him force her to stay when she wanted to leave? She recalled his voice when he had said that he had failed. It hadn't sounded like him, and it wasn't him! He had only said that to try and get Tanya's co-operation. He had no intention of failing. It would have hurt his pride if he had been unable to keep his promise to her father, and that was really all that it amounted to, and had nothing to do with his wanting to watch out for her future.

Tanya's expression was grim as she handed the form she had just completed back to the girl for checking. The girl, who had been somewhat startled by Tanya's expression, said hastily, 'It's fine, Miss Hume, don't worry about it. They're quite easy once you get the hang of them.'

Tanya blinked at the girl for a moment or so before she realised that she was referring to the work, and then gave her an apologetic smile. 'As you say, it's just a question of getting used to it,' she said quietly.

The same, she thought later that day as she left the offices, could be said for her new situation. She had to get used to it, for the next six months at least, and she fervently wished she knew what she could do when the six months were up. One thing was certain, she would not be staying on at Orchard Farm. Her eyes lingered on the familiar structure of her home as she arrived within the home boundary. The greyish stone walls of the house with its slightly pointed roof of red slates seemed to welcome her back, and she bleakly recalled the sheer happiness she had felt on her return home after the constant travelling. She had had no idea then that her stay was once again to be a brief one, but this time she would go for good. She wondered if Kade would move into Orchard House when he had bought her out. She gave a weary shrug. He would have to, there was Connie to consider. There was no point in keeping two establishments going, but that was no worry of hers, she thought, as she made her way down the paved drive bordered with flower beds and followed the path round the front of the house to the back quarters and the large kitchen where Connie would be preparing the evening meal.

On her entry into the kitchen Connie, in the middle of putting a finishing touch to the pastry she had just placed over a pie dish, gave her a quick anxious look. 'How did it go?' she asked quietly.

Tanya tried to give her a reassuring smile, but it appeared as more of a grimace. 'Oh, fine,' she said lightly, but on seeing Connie's frown deepen she exclaimed, 'Terrible, if you want the truth. And the truth,' she went on grimly, 'seems to be something everyone wants to keep from me.' She looked at Connie, now wiping her floured hands on a dishcloth. 'Did you know that Kade practically owns the place?' she demanded.

Connie looked away from her accusing eyes and

studied the pie she had just finished, and it seemed to remind her that it had to be put into the oven, and she did this before replying to Tanya. 'I'm not surprised,' she said in a flat unemotional voice as she straightened up from the oven, then turned to look at Tanya. 'It's a pity you were away at that time,' she remarked slowly. 'You might have understood how things were. I told you that Kade had a bad time of it, so did your dad. He left the running of the business to Kade.' She pursed her lips. 'I know one thing though, that if it hadn't been for Kade you wouldn't have had a home to come back to. Why don't you try being grateful instead of condemning? If you think Kade took advantage of the fact that your father had lost interest in the business then you'd better think again.'

Her eyes left Tanya's, and she looked out of the kitchen window towards the high shrubbery that protected the kitchen garden. 'No, I'm not surprised at all,' she went on. 'Your father started playing the stock markets. There's a rich killing if you know what you're doing, but if you don't,' she shrugged, 'then you go broke overnight.' She looked back at the despondent Tanya who was studying her small sandalled feet as if she had a feeling that she knew what was coming next. 'I loved your mother, but there was no denying that she hadn't the slightest idea of how to handle money. She'd never had to, you see, everything was settled for her, all she had to do was forward the bills, and I have a feeling that those bills got larger as time went on.'

She had no need to spell it out, Tanya could guess the rest. Kade had said as much, hadn't he? she thought bitterly. She had been just as much to blame as her mother. It had never occurred to her to question that side of things, but if she had, she thought wretchedly, it wouldn't have got her anywhere. Her mother would have shrugged the query off as if it had been bad taste for Tanya to even think about such things.

'It's not your fault, pet,' said Connie, shrewdly guessing the thoughts going through Tanya's mind. 'Remember, I knew your mother.' Her eyes misted over in memory. 'She was adorable, and lived in a world of her own. If she had known—well, she would have done something about it. I know she would, but she just didn't think,' she ended lamely.

Tanya nodded dumbly. 'Well, that's that,' she said after a pregnant silence. 'I've promised to stay on for six months until I make up my mind what to do.'

'Make up your mind what you want to do?' repeated Connie in astonishment. 'You mean you're seriously considering leaving?' she demanded incredulously.

Tanya looked back at her with raised brows. 'See it from my point of view, Connie,' she said quietly. 'It's about time I stood on my own two feet. Oh, Kade wants me to stay, to work my way up the ladder of success, he gave his word to Father, you see,' she added bitterly. 'He doesn't particularly like me, Connie, and I'm not too keen on him. It doesn't look much like a recipe for success, does it?' she queried ironically. 'And besides that,' she ended furiously, 'I'm sick and tired of being "watched over" or "coddled". Whichever way you put it, it's a miserable situation to be in, and the sooner I do something about it the better. I want to be able to make my own decisions, and not have them made for me as they have been for as long as I can remember.'

Connie started to say something, but Tanya forestalled her with a quick, 'I know what you're going to say, and although I have good reason to be grateful to Kade, I'm not feeling particularly grateful at the moment. As for the next six months——' She rushed from the kitchen, leaving a very worried Connie staring at the slammed kitchen door.

CHAPTER FOUR

AFTER listening to another stern lecture from Connie the following morning about not rushing her fences, and giving herself time to work out her problems, Tanya left for the offices in a despondent mood. A night's worrying over what she was going to do when the six months were up had brought her no nearer to a solution, apart from the obvious one that she should do exactly what Kade had suggested she should do, and work her way up to a working partnership with him.

As things were at that moment in time it appeared that she had no other choice but to do just that and no amount of wishful thinking would alter the situation. It was of small consolation to remember that she was doing what her father had wanted her to do either. Since her return, Tanya had undergone such a battering of emotions that she only wanted to be free of the past and not to be forced to honour any obligations placed upon her.

If her father had known the true state of affairs, she very much doubted if he would have expected her to carry on under those conditions, but as the thought was there she had a sneaking feeling that she was wrong on that point. He would expect her to do what Kade wanted her to do. He had trusted him to carry out his wishes.

The white walls of the office buildings loomed up in front of her as she passed Kade's chalet, and as if it was he and not the innocuous-looking low building of the chalet, Tanya glared at it. He was an early starter, she knew, and would be on the rounds of the orchard inspecting his crops. She no longer thought of the farm in possessive terms, particularly when recalling Kade's blunt observance on her income hardly matching her past life style.

Melanie, too, was said to be a keen starter, and had secured lodgings for herself in the home of one of the senior members of staff who lived a mile or so away from the works, in order to make an early start.

At the thought of the lovely brunette, Tanya almost stopped in her tracks. She had been detailed to work with her and the prospect was hardly a pleasant one. If Kade had guessed that it had been Melanie who had, as Kade had put it, flung her into the mire of the past— Tanya took a deep breath, the polar regions would hold more welcome for her!

When she recalled Melanie's spiteful outburst that day, and her assumption that Kade was raring to be off, she felt a little better about things. Melanie, it seemed, was not quite as au fait with Kade's personal life as she had thought she was. She had not known that he owned the farm for one thing, and if she had known him as well as Tanya had once thought she did, then she would have known of his admitted attachment to the farm and his reluctance to go back to city life.

Perhaps it was wishful thinking on Melanie's part, for Tanya knew that she came from Hobart and probably missed the hubbub of city life. It couldn't have been much fun for her stuck out in the country as she was now, not if she preferred the bright lights of the city, where she would no doubt have plenty of willing escorts for parties. Tanya gave a short sigh on this thought. Plenty of escorts, but not Kade, and it was Kade that she was after, Tanya had learned that much within a few weeks of her return. Working as she had been with the lower grades of office staff it had been impossible for her not to hear the snippets of news passed down the grapevine, particularly since Melanie was not popular with the staff.

When Tanya walked into the secretary's office prepared to face a seething Melanie, she was surprised to find a pretty redhead seated at Melanie's desk and affording her a welcoming smile. 'Hi!' she said cheerfully, 'I'm Linda Martin, and you must be Miss Hume. Kade told me to expect you. I understand you're learning the ropes,' she indicated a desk placed against the wall near the large filing cabinet. 'I haven't had much time to get acclimatised myself as yet,' she confided to the astonished Tanya, 'but I think you'll find most of the files that Kade said you'd want to study in there.'

Tanya followed Linda's gaze to the filing cabinet and then looked back at Linda again, the surprise clearly visible in her wide eyes. She didn't have to ask the question so plainly mirrored in them.

'Er—Melanie's been relieved of her post,' Linda said, with a slight twinkle in her eye.

'But I don't understand,' said Tanya in a puzzled way. 'I don't remember meeting you before, and I thought I'd met all the staff.'

'Well, I expect you did,' replied Linda with an amused inflection in her voice. 'I'm from Kellings, the other side of the valley,' she added. 'You wouldn't remember me, but I used to see you at some of the parties we used to go to when we were children. My father worked for Mr Kelling in those days, he works for Kade now that he's bought the farm, sort of manager,' she volunteered cheerfully, 'and I'm the office help. I'm filling in until Kade can get a replacement for Melanie.'

Tanya frowned. Her childhood seemed a long way away, and she couldn't ever remember seeing Linda before, but judged that she would be several years older than her.

Seeing the frown, Linda confirmed this with an infectious smile. 'You wouldn't remember, you were always too busy dodging out of Connie Dean's watchful eye. I can remember thinking how I'd hate to have someone keep an eye on me like that when I went to parties.' She gave another smile. 'But then I wasn't a land-owner's daughter, and I was mighty thankful, I can tell you.'

Tanya smiled back at her. 'I hope the replacement takes her time,' she said quietly. 'I think we're going to to get on.'

In the days that followed, Tanya's assumption that she and Linda would become firm friends proved correct, and Tanya found herself hoping that no replacement would be found for the secretary's job. From several things that she had heard from Linda about Melanie, Tanya realised that the farms had been in constant touch. Kade would ring up each day from Orchard Farm and issue instructions for consignments or want reports on the inspection of the fruit trees. If he could afford the time, then he would make a visit, but otherwise he would leave matters in the capable hands of his staff. Any new developments were reported immediately to Orchard Farm for Kade's attention, and Melanie would take the original message if he were not available at the time.

'I only saw Melanie once,' said Linda as they took a

break for coffee a few days after she had taken over from Melanie. 'Kade brought her down with him as he wanted some figures copied out for later study.' Her brown eyes narrowed as she recalled the event. 'I thought she was lovely,' she said frankly, 'but so snooty. If you didn't know she was only a secretary you'd think she owned the place. Mind you, she wouldn't act like that when Kade was around, she was all smiles and sweetness then.' She frowned. 'It didn't take us long to get her measure, though. If she thought you were getting a bit more attention from Kade than she was, then she'd make trouble for you.' She grinned impishly at Tanya. 'You should have heard the way she went for me when Kade came down two days running! We'd got a suspicious-looking growth on one of our trees and there was quite a scare about it at the time. Kade got an expert up from Hobart to take a look at it, and luckily it was quite harmless, but there had been reports of a blight around, and Kade was taking no chances. Not that Melanie thought about that side of it. She was convinced that I was blinking my eyelashes at him and luring him away from business.' She held out her slim white hand and gazed at the solitaire on the third finger of her left hand. 'I told her straight that I was happily engaged, thank you very much, and had no designs on the boss. As a matter of fact,' she confided to Tanya, 'I'd only got engaged the previous evening and was still seeing stars,' she grinned. 'If you know what I mean. Oh, sure, Kade's good-looking, and has what it takes, I guess, but I'd rather settle for my Bill. I can live with him, but a man like Kade would take some living up to, wouldn't he?' she said simply.

Tanya hastily changed the subject by asking her how long Melanie had worked for Kade.

'I believe she started working for him shortly after he came here,' replied Linda. 'I've a feeling he met her in Hobart, and offered her the job. She may have been working for his father, she seemed to know a lot about his home background,' she added ruminatingly.

'Do you know why Kade removed her?' asked Tanya tentatively, as she wasn't sure how much Linda knew of the past.

Linda shrugged casually. 'She'd been getting a bit too big for her shoes, I guess,' she said. 'Although it's rumoured that she put her delicate little paw into something that didn't concern her. Anyway,' she concluded happily, 'I'm glad Kade chose me to fill in. I'm going to ask him to make it permanent. Bill and I are saving like mad to buy a small property this side of the valley, and this job is better paid than the last one. Do you think he'll agree?' she asked Tanya doubtfully.

'Oh, I'm sure he will,' said Tanya warmly. 'It's not that easy to get someone who knows the job,' she added. She did not offer to speak to Kade about it, and she hoped Linda would not be offended by this. She had had very little to do with Kade since she had begun work in the main offices. To her relief she had found that her worry that she would be constantly thrown into his company had been pleasantly forestalled by the realisation that he did not spend a lot of time in the office, and allowed only an hour from nine to ten for queries and dictation, then he was off on his business rounds of the orchards.

Now and again, he would pause on his way out of his office and enquire how Tanya was getting on with the job of familiarising herself with the files of the firm's customers, and she would give a polite if stiff reply, that she was coping.

Linda had watched these exchanges with a slightly puzzled air, particularly as Tanya was the only one in the whole works who referred to Kade as Mr Player. When she had got to know Tanya better she asked her about this. 'It does sound odd, Tanya, when you call Kade Mr Player. I mean, no one else does, do they?' she queried curiously.

Tanya's lips set on this innocent-sounding query. She didn't want to snub Linda as she could understand her curiosity—nevertheless, she had no intention of discussing the matter. She shrugged casually. 'It's just that I always think of him as Mr Player,' she lied, and hoped that Linda would leave it at that, but she was doomed to disappointment.

'You don't like him, do you?' replied Linda musingly. 'And that's odd, too. Everyone likes Kade.' She flung Tanya an assessing look. 'I wouldn't say you were the sort of person who took instant likes or dislikes to anyone—unless you had cause to. You sort of freeze up whenever he's in the room, I've noticed that much,' she continued in a wondering way.

Tanya sent her a warning look from her grey-green eyes. 'Don't make a mystery out of it, Linda, there's a dear,' she said quietly. That was all she said, but it had the desired effect, and Linda gave her an apologetic smile and started talking about the house she and her Bill had their eyes on, and Tanya was able to draw a tiny sigh of relief for safely scrambling over that particular hurdle.

After a fortnight in the office, Tanya found her happy sojourn in Linda's company was to come to an end. Kade altered her schedule for the next stage of her indoctrination into the firm's affairs, and she found that she would be accompanying him on his daily rounds of inspection of the orchards. The thought of being constantly in his company made Tanya wish that she had had the courage to walk out of Orchard Farm as she had planned to do after that traumatic interview with Kade, but she had given her word—or to be more precise, she corrected herself bitterly, a promise had been forced out of her.

Far from sympathising with Tanya, Linda had given her a mischievous grin and commented teasingly, 'You might just end up calling him Kade!'

Although many things were likely, Tanya told herself the following morning, as she saddled the horse Kade had lent her for the round of the orchards, Linda's bright forecast on the future relationship between her and Kade blossoming into friendship was definitely not one of them. Linda didn't know the whole truth, and Tanya had been devoutly grateful for this. Kade had said that he had clamped down on the gossip concerning the past, and it said a lot for his authority and integrity that he had succeeded in confining it to within the boundaries of the home farm. Tanya might not like him, but she did concede this.

At the sound of hoofbeats in the near distance, Tanya mounted the bay gelding and rode out to meet Kade who would be impatient to be off.

As she followed Kade's big black stallion past the office section and out to the orchards, Tanya's thoughts went back to the past, and she recalled Kade's words that at heart she was still the child that used to follow him round the orchards all those years ago. But it wasn't years, it was aeons, she thought sadly, things were so different, not at all the way she had imagined them in her memory when she had been away. The few weeks that she had spent in the past with her father during her allotted period of stay each year had been spent as a holiday vacation. He had taken her out on sightseeing trips to Sydney, and they had visited the home beauty spots. Tanya's plea of 'Couldn't we stay at home this time?' had been of no avail, for he would always smile and say that he had saved up this period of time exclusively for her, and that he enjoyed taking her places, and that it was his holiday too.

She gulped as the memories washed over her. How plain everything was when you were given the answers! Now she could understand her father's anxiety to keep her away from the farm, never letting her stay around there long enough to strike up a friendship with any-one who might unwittingly make some reference to the past. She could also understand why he had wanted to imprint upon her that her own country still had much to offer in the way of outstanding beauty that was not man-made, but gifts of nature.

So Tanya's memories of the farm had remained the same as she had had as a child, but now she was seeing it from an entirely different angle, and a rather jaun-diced one at that.

As a van loaded with boxes hooted as it passed by them a few moments later, Tanya realised with a start that it was the picking season. She had had so much on her mind that such an event had gone unnoticed by her until now. There was further evidence of this when they arrived at the first acre, where hordes of men and women were engaged in picking the rosy-hued fruit that clustered in groups on the healthy-looking trees.

Some sang as they worked, and others held animated conversations with their workmates working alongside of them. The atmosphere was one of cheerful bustle and an unhurried urgency to get the fruit off to the sorting department and away to its final destination.

Kade's popularity with the workers was evident as they passed through the lines of activity. Tanya was surprised by the fact that Kade knew and greeted each worker by name, although there were so many of them —there had to be to cope with the vast acreage to be worked.

The cheery greetings were extended to Tanya too, and as most of the helpers had been with the firm for a great many years they would know who she was without being told. Returning their greetings, Tanya felt a glow of warmth flow through her for the first time since she had returned home.

When Kade dismounted and strode over towards a group of women industriously engaged in picking the firm fruit, Tanya followed suit presuming that that was what he would expect her to do. As her eyes followed his tall figure, and then rested on the group of women he was about to join, she noticed the way they automatically patted the bright kerchiefs they wore on their heads, much in the way they would pat a hair-style into place, as if making sure that their appearance was presentable. She also noticed the almost reverent way they watched him select an apple from the box that lay at their feet and minutely examine the fruit. When he replaced it with a curt satisfied nod it seemed to Tanya that they all relaxed, as if it would have been their fault if the fruit had been found wanting.

Kade repeated this action at random intervals right

through the upper acres of orchards and the same hushed atmosphere would prevail during the inspection. As before, Tanya would stand beside him and just watch proceedings, and only once did he call her attention to one particular tree whose fruits were just as healthy as the others, but were smaller. 'This is the sort of thing we watch out for,' he commented to her, and turned to the foreman anxiously watching the inspection. 'Look up last year's charts, Len,' he ordered. 'I'm pretty certain you'll find the crop from this one slightly under norm, might be as well to give it a soil test and a change of feed next season.'

The foreman nodded in agreement with this diagnosis; and Tanya watched Kade's long lean fingers gently run over the smooth skin of the apple. If he had been stroking the skin of the woman he loved, his touch could not have been more gentle. At this thought she felt acutely embarrassed and moved away on the pretence of examining other apples from the same tree.

To Tanya, the morning had been an experience. Apples to her were a fruit to be picked when ready, and eaten when required, and that was all there was to it— or had been before her introduction into the growing of the fruit and its attendant problems. The trees had to be sprayed every year to keep them free from pests, and at the acreage covered, it was a pretty expensive operation. There were also records to be kept of each year's crop, and a certainty of a plentiful harvest to ensure a healthy profit after the deduction of the seasonal workers' pay.

The majority of the pickers were seasonal workers who came year after year, and the general atmosphere was one of feverish but happy activity. As most of them came from the surrounding hamlets, they all knew each other, and it was like a yearly family outing. Food was provided from Orchard House, and wooden tables with trestle seats were placed at convenient points throughout the orchards to serve the army of helpers.

It reminded Tanya of a national park area, where picnic sites were placed for the use of tourists passing through, only here they were workers and not tourists, and were surrounded by acres of rosy fruit waiting to be picked. When one considered all the angles, it was quite a big business and not just a case of waiting on the sidelines for the fruit to ripen, as Tanya had once mistakenly thought, but then she had had nothing to do with the business side of the farm.

When Kade told her at midday that they would be having lunch at Orchard House, she was slightly taken aback and wondered with a certain amount of misgiving if this was to be the start of a new relationship between them. He had never before honoured her with his presence at the meal table, and she wondered if this was Connie's doing. She must have asked Kade to lunch the previous evening, when he had brought the bay gelding over for her use the next day.

He could have refused, she thought crossly, and wondered why he had accepted. She looked longingly at the picnic tables and the helpers now gathering round to sort out the large hampers of food provided, and wished she could stay to lunch with them. It wouldn't be so embarrassing for her since she could not imagine what she and Kade would have to talk about, unless it was to be a working lunch.

They had almost reached the driveway to the house when an expensive-looking car emerged from the drive and drew up in front of them. A tall thin man then un-folded himself from the driving seat and came towards them smiling. 'Hi! I was told you were out on the rounds. I'm Charlie Page,' he volunteered, looking at Kade. 'We usually do our business by phone, but as I was in these parts I thought I'd look you up.'

Kade dismounted and held a welcoming hand out to the man. 'Pleased to meet you,' he drawled. 'I trust our last consignment was satisfactory?'

Tanya, who had remained seated, had a sudden hope that Kade and his unexpected visitor would start on a long discussion that necessitated his absence from lun-cheon, but she was doomed to disappointment.

'This is my partner,' said Kade abruptly, introducing Tanya to Charlie Page, and dismissing any chance of her making her departure.

The man gave her a wide cheery grin and walked over towards her, forcing her to dismount, and then held a large horny hand towards her. 'Very pleased to meet you, Mrs Player,' he said happily.

'I'm not Mrs Player!' exclaimed Tanya, after the short shocked silence that followed. 'Just a working partner,' she managed to get out, as casually as she was able to, but her voice echoed her outraged feelings as did her wide eyes as they flew from Mr Page to Kade, who appeared to be thoroughly enjoying her discom-fort.

'Thanks, anyway, for the compliment,' he said to the now embarrassed man. 'You haven't answered my query, is everything okay?' he asked, casually turning the conversation to other matters, and relieving him from the necessity of having to make profuse apologies all round.

Tanya did not take in the rest of the conversation,

she was too busy digesting Kate's sarcastic, 'Thanks for the compliment,' remark. She did remember that Mr Page was asked to lunch but tactfully refused, and she wished he had accepted, since that would have made it a business lunch, and would have considerably eased the situation, as far as she was concerned anyway. However, far from being unsatisfied with past consignments he wanted to double up on past orders, and having told Kade this, he went on his way, favouring Tanya with an apologetic smile before he drove off.

On their arrival at the house, Connie took one look at Tanya's tight expression and hurriedly announced that lunch would be on the table as soon as they were ready for it, then dashed back into the kitchen.

Tanya escaped to her room to take a quick shower, leaving Kade to use the outside washhouse facilities. She lingered over her toilet as long as she dared, and when she couldn't put it off any longer, she made her way down to the dining room to find a sardonic Kade awaiting her arrival.

'Don't take it so hard,' drawled Kade, as he took in her set expression as she took her place at the table. 'Anyone would think you cared!' he added sardonically.

Tanya helped herself to some salad from a bowl on the table and willed herself not to lose her temper. The derision in his voice cut right to the heart of her unhappiness. She could ignore his blunt summing up of her feelings and pretend that she didn't know what he was talking about, but it wouldn't work, she thought dully. She would only be wasting her time. That was something else she had learned about Kade, he preferred the blunt approach.

Somehow she managed to keep her voice steady as

she replied coldly, 'Perhaps in future it would be better if you referred to me as Miss Hume. It sounds better, doesn't it?' she added acidly.

'You're damn right it does!' he answered savagely. 'Although no one but a clothhead would have mistaken my meaning. I know some men prefer them young, but I don't happen to be one of them,' he added viciously. 'So don't get any fancy ideas, will you?' he tacked on for good measure.

Tanya almost dropped her knife and fork at his cool assumption that she was about to indulge in daydreams. When she recalled the way he had turned her earlier rejection of him into a ploy to gain his attention, her amazement turned to fury. 'It wouldn't occur to you, of course, that nothing was further from my mind,' she replied in a low vibrant voice. 'My mother married a man who was too old for her and I've no intention of making the same mistake. You can rest assured, Mr Player, that I'm not about to repeat history—not now —or at any time. Just credit me with some common sense in future, and stop seeing yourself as a hunted prize on the matrimonial market—where I'm concerned anyway. That way we'll get on fine!' she advised him coldly.

Her words made Kade's blue eyes open a shade wider, and she knew she had scored a hit. 'That's how you see me, is it?' he queried softly, out of now narrowed eyes.

Tanya's grey-green eyes had now a definite green tinge in them as she met his. 'Frankly, yes,' she replied acidly. Seeing an amused glint in his eyes, and suspecting the reason behind his amusement, she wanted to slap his handsome arrogant face. 'Do you remember telling me that I was still the child who used to follow you around the orchards on a pony?' she demanded in a tight voice. 'Well, I'll tell you something now. You were right in one sense; I'm still the same person I was then, and I can still remember the way you snubbed every move of mine towards friendship. But it didn't stop at that, did it? When I returned home I got as much welcome from you as I might have got had I been a warring headhunter!'

Her voice was not quite as steady as it had been before, but she made herself go on. 'If I ever needed a friend, I needed one then, but what did I get?' she said bitterly. 'The same old treatment that I received all those years ago—with just as little reason—at least,' she paused, and drew in a ragged breath. 'I didn't know the reason then, but I do now. Melanie did me a favour when she summed it all up in a few well-chosen words.' Her eyes reflected the dislike she felt for him as she continued: 'She told me you'd had enough trouble with my mother to risk tangling with me.'

Kade's swift indrawn breath was not lost on her, and it gave her the courage to go on. She was no match for him; with a word or a look he could scythe through her defences, and she knew it, but if she could pierce through that supreme confidence of his just once, then she would be well satisfied. 'As for daydreaming, as you so bluntly put it just now, do you honestly think I'm that much of a fool?' She laid her knife and fork down on her plate and pushed it away from her abruptly. Whatever appetite she might have had had now deserted her.

'Eat your lunch,' commanded Kade loftily, just as though she were the child of yesteryear.

Tanya did no such thing, but reached for the coffee

pot and found Kade's strong fingers closing over hers. 'I said, eat your lunch,' he repeated firmly. 'You're much too thin as it is, and you'll need some refuelling to replace all that ammunition you've just shot me down with. Okay,' he said abruptly, his hand now clenched over her wrist to prevent her from carrying out her intention of leaving the table and escaping from his presence. 'You've had your say, now you'll hear mine.'

She had no choice but to do as he had said. He still had an iron hold on her wrist, and although she was forced to sit down on her chair again, he retained his hold on her as if certain that she would make a bolt for the door if he released her, but he did lessen his hold sufficiently for it not to cause her any discomfort.

It was during this highly charged interval that Connie chose to look in to see if they wanted any more coffee, but at Kade's growled, 'Later, Connie,' she made a hasty retreat back into the kitchen.

'So in your estimation I notch up a fair number of points for the Brute of the Year contest,' he began harshly, as the door swung to behind Connie. 'So now I'm saying sorry in the only way I know how, and you'd better accept it,' he said quietly. 'I'm not likely to repeat it again. I guess I didn't make things clear enough the other day, although I did hope you'd see things from my point of view.' His voice was much gentler now. 'As for keeping my distance from you when you were a kid—I had to—as things were then, I couldn't risk giving your mother a chance to capitalise on any friendly overtures in any direction, and that included you.'

His gaze went beyond Tanya and rested on a framed photograph of her mother and father taken on their

wedding day. 'As for not giving you an uproarious welcome when you returned,' he went on gruffly, 'well, I
admit to being at fault there, but old memories die
hard, especially the bad ones. Things were never the
same again between your father and me after you and
your mother left. Oh, he trusted me to run his business
for him, but he was human enough to wonder if I'd
encouraged your mother. He could never be sure, you
see.'

His eyes left the photograph and came back to Tanya.
'After what he'd done for my family, how do you think
I felt about that?' he demanded in a low voice. 'If there
was one man I respected above all others, it was your
father. How can you answer unspoken accusations?' he
queried bitterly. 'I could have yelled myself hoarse in
repudiating them if I'd been given a chance, but you
can't yell at intangibles, things that are sensed but
never said. Far better to have it out and done with, it's
kinder that way,' he added on a weary note.

He released his hold on her wrist and gave her a hard
searching look. 'I'm grateful you didn't bottle it all up
and gave it straight from the shoulder. I guess the past
has been as rough on you as it was for me. Shall we start
again,' he asked her softly, 'and see if we can't make a
better deal between us?'

Tanya wanted to weep. If only he had said all this
before! It was a little late now for him to realise that
he had not been the only one who had suffered in the
past. As much as she wished that she could accept his
belated peace offering, she felt that it was too late.

If Kade altered his approach to her and began treat-
ing her with respect, and with the kind of humble
humility that had been in his last words, then she

would be totally lost. She might have convinced him that she had no aspirations to become closer to him, and had no romantic notions where he was concerned, but the sad fact of the matter was that she still loved him. Only by whipping up a hate relationship with him could she survive. She was not insensible to the fact that it would mean more heartache for her, but either way, she couldn't win. A scathing and sardonic Kade was preferable to the other side of his personality, that had shown a kind and gentle understanding that had surprised her. If he ever found out that she loved him— her heart missed a beat on the thought as she acknowledged the salient if painful realisation that there could be no such relationship between them. If Tanya had been unhappy before, she was doubly so now, and wanted an end to the whole miserable situation. It wasn't a case of cowardice—as she was sure Kade would see it when she reasserted her wish to leave Orchard Farm. It was plainly and simply a case of survival against overwhelming odds.

CHAPTER FIVE

TANYA found herself completely unable to look at him as she gave him her answer. She stared down at her hands now twisted together in her lap. 'It won't work, Kade,' she said slowly, and was surprised how firm her voice was. 'There's too much behind us,' she added heavily. 'You said that you were grateful that I'd been honest with you—well, I'm going to be more honest now. I promised to stay for six months, and I'm going to keep my word, but after that I intend to leave.'

She darted a quick look at him and saw the familiar stiffening of his strong jaw. 'I've somewhere to go,' she said quickly. 'I was offered a home when Mother died—and the offer's still open—it will always be there,' she added significantly. 'I know you want to keep your promise to my father, but if he were still here I'm sure that under the circumstances he would understand.' She gave Kade a brittle smile. 'You said I belonged here, but you were wrong. I don't belong—I stopped belonging when Mother walked out all those years ago.'

'And where exactly do you think you belong?' he asked harshly. 'To the place you're going?' Before she could answer, he added pithily, 'And I want to know just where this place is.'

Tanya's brows raised at this; he might have been her father or her elder brother, such was his presumption that he had a right to know. In a way, she conceded, he had a right to know, and it might as well be now. 'In

Oregon,' she said quietly, and on seeing his eyes nar-
row, she nodded complacently. 'Yes, he was one of my
mother's friends, so I'll be well looked after.'

'Why didn't you accept his offer earlier?' he queried,
his blue stare pierced into her wide eyes. 'You didn't,
did you? You came back home!' There was an emphasis
on the word home and Tanya did not miss that.

'Because I didn't know at that time what I really
wanted,' she lied. 'I was upset and unable to think
straight. I needed time to work things out.' She took a
deep breath. 'Well, I've thought things out now, and
have decided to accept his offer.'

'I take it he's a bachelor?' Kade commented sourly,
and continued without her confirmation. 'That was six
months back, what happens if he's got himself fixed up
by now?' he asked sardonically.

Tanya's lovely eyes showed her puzzlement at the
question. 'Fixed up?' she repeated slowly.

'Come, come,' jeered Kade, now back to form again.
'He was courting your mother, wasn't he? She had the
kind of looks that attracts them in droves. So—like I
said—what happens if he's got his eye on someone
else? Your presence would be a trifle embarrassing for
him, to put it mildly. Have you thought of that?' he
shot out at her.

Tanya's eyes sparked shoots of green fire as his im-
plication reached through her earlier puzzlement. She
needed no whipping-up of hatred towards him now; he
had given her the spur she wanted. Her shocked senses
wondered how she could ever have thought she was in
love with him. With a few caustic words he had managed to label her mother as a rapacious manhunter,
and Lloyd Warren as a loser in the marriage stakes and

now on the trail for a successor. That was bad enough in itself, she thought furiously, but when he had added the further indignity of making her feel the unwanted left-over from the liaison between Lloyd and her mother, her hate towards him became a live sensation. What would he know of such relationships? He'd been too busy protecting himself from his adoring female fans to learn about love, and that it could be a beautiful thing. Tanya was certain that her mother would have married Lloyd had she been able to do so, but she had put her daughter's happiness before her own when she had agreed to abide by the decision made by Tanya's father never to remarry.

There was cold fury in her voice as she replied, 'I don't think that's any business of yours. You might have managed my father's affairs, but I refuse to discuss my private life with you. I'm going to Oregon and that's an end to it.'

'Want to bet on it?' replied Kade with eyes that glinted dangerously. 'When you summed me up a while ago you forgot to add one other ingredient to my list of bad points. I'd prove a bad loser. I've never lost a fight yet, and I don't intend to start now. I said you belonged here, and I meant just that. By fair or foul means I mean to prove that to you within the stated time limit—so don't think you can run out on me. If my guess about the Oregon connection is right, then you'd do well to listen to me and make up your mind to settle down to the job of running the business.'

He gave the gasping Tanya a long considering look. 'It's my guess you've a lot to learn about life,' he commented quietly. 'You'd find yourself in a hell of a mess if you walked into the kind of situation I've outlined.

I've an idea that that was why you turned him down before, and if you're honest, you'll admit it.'

'I'll admit no such thing!' replied Tanya, incensed. 'There was a reason why I turned his offer down, but not the one you're hinting at, that I'd cramp his style—that's what you meant, isn't it?' she said furiously. 'Well, you're wrong again. He's not a bit like the sort of person you're making him out to be. In point of fact he was the one man I wished my mother had married!'

Her blazing eyes met the cool sardonic ones of Kade, and she knew that he was not convinced, and the knowledge made her even more furious. 'And what about you, Mr Player?' she bit out tersely. 'Won't I cramp your style? You're a bachelor too, so the same goes for you!'

Again she noticed that sudden widening of his eyes and felt a spurt of satisfaction that she had managed to score a point there.

Kade's eyes were no longer sardonic but furious as he bit back harshly. 'If you mean what I think you mean, then I'd advise you to choose your words with more care,' he warned. 'We were discussing your mother's friend. As for cramping my style—you're not up to my weight.' His eyes narrowed speculatively as he added slowly, 'It's my opinion your mother kept you well away from any emotional involvement—after what happened to her she'd make certain history wasn't repeated,' he ended scathingly.

Tanya blinked in shock. She hadn't meant it to sound as if she was vying for a place in his love life, but either he had deliberately misinterpreted her words or he really thought that that was what was behind her challenge. As for his blunt comments on her mother keeping her free from involvements—well—he was right on that score, but she wasn't going to give him the satisfaction of knowing that!

Her small chin jutted out in a defiant gesture as she said suggestively, 'She couldn't be around all the time,' and tried to assume a cool demeanour as she met his searching eyes.

His lips thinned as he drawled softly, 'If I believed what you're hinting at then I'd agree with your haring off to Oregon.' His eyes rested on her soft full lips now clamped together in temper. 'I wouldn't mind betting you've never been kissed,' he remarked in a casual mocking way. His eyes laughed at her as she made an involuntary move away from him. 'Don't worry, I'm not about to indoctrinate you into such pastimes. We'll save that for a more suitable applicant.'

Again Tanya caught the inflection of the big brother act, and she wished she could relieve some of her fury by pummelling him with her fists, but it would be just as effective as hitting the wall behind him, only she would suffer. How dared he assume that he had the right to choose her boy-friends for her! 'Why waste all that experience of yours?' she cut back bitterly, without realising what she was saying. 'Why not throw it in as part and parcel of the business course? You never know —it might come in handy!'

There was a small shocked silence after this, and Tanya's cheeks flamed as the full realisation of her outburst reached through her infuriated senses. How could she have lowered herself like that? If he took her up on it, then she wouldn't be waiting for the time limit to be up, she'd be off on the next plane to Oregon for a certainty!

Kade stood surveying her flushed cheeks through hooded eyes. 'The day may come when you'll come to wish you hadn't said that,' he said warningly, then turned abruptly away from her and walked to the door. 'If you've finished your lunch, we've the lower acres to inspect.'

Tanya closed her eyes; she wanted to shout out after him that she hadn't meant what she'd said, and would he please forget it, but when she opened her eyes again he'd left the room, and there was nothing for her to do but follow him. As for forgetting, it was a little too late for that. A man like that never forgot, and whatever the future held for her now, she had brought it upon herself.

The afternoon rounds of the lower orchards were decidedly different from the morning rounds. Tanya was hardly given a breathing space. Each time Kade inspected the crop of fruit from selected trees, she was told what he was looking for and why. In what seemed a remarkably short period of time she was given the history of the apple industry in the island, that went back to Governor Bligh of the *Bounty*, credited with bringing the fruit to the Island.

For all Tanya cared the seeds could have been dropped by the birds, but her wide grey eyes showed none of her thoughts as she met Kade's determined blue ones.

His attitude towards her now was one of teacher to student. A teacher who was determined that his pupil should do well, and that she would pass the finals if he had to push her through them! There was more at stake than his pride, she mused, for without meaning to she had offered him a challenge and he had accepted it.

When it came down to brass tacks it was a case of his will against hers. It was a fight that she dared not lose, even if it meant breaking her word and taking off for Oregon. On this thought she sighed inwardly. She didn't want to break her word; her mother had run away from her problems instead of facing up to them, and had created more problems and more unhappiness for all concerned. Tanya's problem was different in that she was free to choose her own destiny—and she chose not to fall into the same emotional trap that had brought so much bitterness in its train.

Her eyes rested on the bright green foliage of the branch that Kade was holding out for her inspection as he gave her another lecture, this time on the spraying of the trees. All this meant nothing to her; her mind was made up and he was just wasting his breath. This thought somewhat alleviated the frustration she had felt during their earlier confrontation. She would play it his way from now on—it was better than being stuck in an office anyway, and she would be a very attentive student. He had said that he meant to win by fair or foul means, hadn't he? What was good enough for him was good enough for her. She would lull him into thinking he had won the fight, and when the time limit was up she would say something soothing on the lines of how interesting it had all been, but now she must be off.

'Are you listening?' demanded Kade, eyeing the sparkle in her eyes as she contemplated her final triumphant exit from Orchard Farm, with a hint of suspicion in his.

Tanya came out of her happy musings with a guilty start, and blinked at Kade, now with a glint in his eye.

'Of course,' she replied hastily, thinking she had to do better than this if her plan was to succeed. 'You were talking about spraying the crops,' she went on hastily, devoutly hoping he would not ask her to give a verbatim report of the subject.

His sardonic reply of, 'So we were,' and his added, 'Well, I guess there's plenty of time,' drawled on what Tanya could only interpret as a warning note, gave her cause to suspect that he was well aware of her intentions and envisaged no trouble in overcoming them.

This thought somewhat dampened her earlier enthusiasm for the fight ahead, but by the time the inspection had finished and they were on the way back to Orchard Farm at the close of the working day, she had recovered her fighting spirit. Oddly enough Kade's own words had brought about her recovery. She remembered what he'd said about her being a fighter, and not being the type to run away. Although it could be argued that he was just saying that to make her agree to stay and see things through, but she knew that he was not a person to utter glib statements, and would certainly not lower his standard to suit the occasion—any occasion—he was too straightforward for that.

When Kade told her that she would be accompanying him to Hobart the next day, Tanya realised that there was more to the business than just inspecting the orchards and making out the accounts. When another and much less palatable thought hit her, she very nearly gave up the fight then and there. It was Kade's cool order that she should pack an evening dress as they would be attending a social function after the conference was ended that started her palpitations.

The plain fact was that she didn't know enough

about the business to know whether he always attended the ensuing social get-together. She had a nasty suspicion that he didn't, but was making a point of doing so for her benefit. She swallowed. If it was for her benefit then he needn't have bothered, but she could hardly say so, could she? not after her rash outburst during lunch. So much for hoping that he would forget her lapse from grace, she thought bitterly as she envisaged an evening in his company.

Her heartbeats increased rapidly at the thought of dancing with him and beat a positive tattoo as she recalled his threatened reminder that one day she would regret her open invitation to him to teach her the wiles of love. It looked as though that 'day' had arrived!

In an effort to stem the rising panic she felt hovering at the back of her senses she made herself go over that all-too-revealing scene again in her mind. The more she thought about it, the worse it looked for her. Only the thought that Kade must have known that she had no idea of just what she was suggesting somewhat calmed her. He had also known that she was completely inexperienced, and most certainly not in his sophisticated grade, in spite of her pathetic attempt to mislead him.

It would be amusing for him to try her out, she thought miserably, and that was all it would be for him. An interesting study into the mind of one Tanya Hume, a little girl cosseted all her life from the big bad world. The worst of it, was that it was the truth. She had never had to fend for herself; she had never been given the opportunity—even now, when she might have made a start, this hard man was making a take-over bid before she had time to find her feet.

The fact that this same hard man filled her dreams

and set her longing for something that was completely unattainable, made the situation even more complicated. It did, however, serve to strengthen her resolve to leave Orchard Farm as soon as the opportunity presented itself. Dreams or no dreams, Tanya was basically a sensible girl, and the thought of a future filled with hopeless longings was not to be contemplated. With Kade constantly near her, and the sound of his deep autocratic voice that could raise her to the heavens, or cast her into the deepest dungeons, there would be little chance of happiness for her.

When Kade called for her the following morning, Tanya was waiting for him. Her overnight case, that held what she hoped would be a suitable dress for the evening's entertainment, stood outside on the verandah to be collected as she left the house.

Her heart gave a little leap as she took in his tall lean figure, dressed now in town wear and looking as well turned out as the moneyed set of people she had spent most of her earlier life with. Not that he ever looked anything but what he was—boss—and master of all he surveyed. He was now surveying her, she noticed, and knew an anxious moment as to whether her finely tailored suit of lime green came up to standard. She still wasn't sure that it did after his curt nod and abrupt, 'Ready?' because of the way his eyes lingered on the frothy bow of her white blouse, and she wondered miserably if she oughtn't to have chosen a more business-looking blouse to go with the suit.

'We'll be late, Connie,' he called out, as he picked up her case and strode towards the car leaving an uncertain Tanya to follow him. She couldn't win whatever she did, she told herself, as she obediently took the front seat that he stood impatiently waiting for her to take and ready to slam the car door after her.

She had made some attempt to make herself look a little older by twisting up her hair and fixing it in a little knot on the top of her head, but the car windows were wide open and fine tendrils of the white-blonde hair kept escaping from the loosely fixed bun, whipping across her face and causing her much irritation.

From time to time she would reach up an impatient hand to remove the offending tendril, and make some effort to secure it back into position. She was just making another futile attempt to catch another wisp that had settled across her left eye when Kade growled; 'For heaven's sake! Either fix it properly, or let it loose!'

Tanya glared at him. What business was it of his how she wore her hair? If it offended him that much, then she would sit in the back seat!

She was about to say as much when he added, still on a note of asperity, 'It doesn't suit you, anyway. You've plenty of time to look your age without trying to hurry up matters. It's not a question of looks, either,' he went on, heedless of Tanya's outraged gasp. 'It's personality that counts. Just be yourself and stop trying to convince everybody that you know it all.'

By everybody, he meant himself, thought Tanya, fuming, and how on earth could he accuse her of trying to impress him? So she had tried to make herself look older, but it hadn't been for his benefit—well, she conceded honestly—only in a roundabout way she had tried to look the part. It was a business trip after all was said and done. She took refuge in sarcasm. 'Not in a very good mood, are we?' she queried sweetly. 'What happened? Did one of your lady friends let you down?' she added acidly, determined to show him that she had no illusions where he was concerned, and the sooner he realised this the sooner he would stop slating her on the personal front.

She knew a spurt of alarm when he glided the big car to a stop in a layby they were about to pass, and switched off the engine with a snap of his strong fingers, then sat back and with narrowed eyes raked the inwardly cringing Tanya who was determined not to show him that she was afraid of him. 'Let's get one thing straight, shall we?' he bit out at her. 'We'll keep personal issues out of this. What I do in my spare time is no concern of yours—and never will be. If you've any sense at all, then you'd do well to remember that.'

'That's fine by me!' retorted Tanya, too furious now to be afraid of him. 'I'll go along with the personal issues as well, just as long as you stick to the rules, too. In future, I want no more personal remarks from you on how, or how not, to style my hair. I'll have it crew cut if the idea takes me!' she declared vehemently. 'As for being myself, that's what I've tried to be, and that's what I'm going on being—and I'm a little tired of your insinuations,' she added heatedly. 'It seems I always have to have an ulterior motive for whatever I do—in your eyes anyhow. As far as I can see,' she concluded bitterly, 'there's one set of rules for you, and an entirely different set for me.'

'Now who's not in a good mood?' countered Kade with a wicked gleam of amusement in his blue eyes. 'Okay, kitten; you can sheath those claws of yours now. It looks as if we're quits. Whatever else this partnership brings, it won't be dull,' he commented in mock solemnity.

Tanya chose to ignore his last comment since she had no intention of going into full partnership with such an autocratic character. 'Don't call me kitten!' she ground out. 'If you're going to call me anything, I'd far rather you called me Miss Hume; that way no one gets any wrong ideas.'

Kade swung the car out of the layby and on to the main road again before flashing her a grim look. 'Very well, your highness,' he said tauntingly. 'If that's the way you want to play it. Just remember that I'm your adviser, and not your knight in shining armour!'

The rest of the journey was continued in a forbidding silence. Tanya, still smarting at his parting shot, wondered why she had ever attempted to fool him over her true feelings for him. It hadn't worked and those last words had proved that beyond doubt. She sighed inwardly. It all went back such a long time; she had loved him before she had even known what the word love meant. Recalling her homecoming six months ago, and the way her eyes had pleaded with him to be kind to her, she could well understand his attitude. One could fall out of love as well as in love, she thought hopefully. She didn't want to go on loving him—it hurt too much, and it hurt her pride. She had four months in which to get him out of her hair, and as her future happiness depended upon it, she had no intention of failing.

She cast a quick surreptitious glance at Kade's grim profile as he turned the car into a spacious car park in the forecourt of a large hotel on the outskirts of Hobart. He was good and mad now and she hoped he stayed that way. You couldn't go on loving someone who marched over your sensitivity with hobnailed boots. It was even worse when that same person was well aware of what he was doing.

'I've booked a day room for us,' Kade said curtly, as they walked towards the hotel entrance. 'The conference is being held here. You've fifteen minutes to freshen up. The meeting starts at ten. I'll meet you in the lobby at five to.'

Tanya's acknowledgement of this terse directive was just as curt as Kade's had been. 'Very well,' she answered stiffly, and accepted the key he had procured for her from the desk and walked to the elevator without giving him a backward glance. As he had not accompanied her she presumed he had other matters to attend to before the meeting started. In all probability he would make for the bar where most of the conference members would have gathered for a talk among themselves.

There had been two keys, she had noticed, and had felt a surge of relief that Kade would not be sharing her room for the rest of the day—as things were, it would have been highly embarrassing for both of them, although she very much doubted if Kade knew what the word meant, much less his having experienced such an emotion.

As soon as she had entered her room, she unpacked her evening dress and hung it up in the large wardrobe provided. She had no worry over the dress being creased as it was of a crease-proof material. Her eyes went over the soft peach folds. It was long-sleeved, with a scalloped neckline, and cunningly designed to suit any occasion. It was not too fussy—nor too plain, and like all very expensive clothes lent an air of correctness to the wearer, thus giving a nervous new young participant in the party a confident boost.

Tanya possessed several such dresses, chosen for her by her mother, who had had an instinctive eye for fashion matched with suitability. Whatever else Tanya might lack in the material sense, it was not clothes. Her wardrobe was well stocked and would see her through to what looked like being a very lean future.

Having hung up the dress, she then turned her attention to her appearance, and gave a slight moue at her untidy hair. She could put it up again, and without the steady breeze that had flowed through the car windows, it should stay in position. However, after she had combed it out, she decided to leave it lying loose in the style she had always worn. It was nothing to do with Kade's remarks, she told herself stoutly; she felt more comfortable like this. If she had really thought about having the style changed she could have had it cut, she mused, as she saw the way it lay curled on her shoulders, and didn't look at all businesslike. Be yourself, had been Kade's sardonic advice, she thought, as she contemplated pulling it back from her face in a ponytail. Well, that was exactly what she would have to do, she thought with exasperation, when she found that it was not long enough to adopt that style either, and impatiently shook it free again and let the soft tendrils once again frame her heart-shaped face.

A glance at her watch told her that it was time that she left the room and went down to the lobby to meet Kade. She wasn't unduly worried about the conference. She hoped that it took up most of the day, but she was worried about the ensuing social activities in which she

envisaged being abandoned by Kade at the first opportunity that presented itself, and wondered what she was
going to do with herself after that. The thought that
she had a room in the hotel gave her much comfort.
She could slip away from the festivities as and when she
liked. On this cheerful thought she lifted her chin a
fraction higher and went down to meet Kade.

CHAPTER SIX

THE conference ended at four, and although Tanya would never have admitted it to Kade, she found it very interesting.

The rising prices of costs and the inevitable follow-through of higher retail prices for the fruit took up most of the business on the agenda. A small section of the fruit farmers were in favour of passing on the extra loading costs direct to the retailer, without a passing thought of the ensuing consequences to the consumers. This would, as Kade had pointed out with reasonable but forceful argument, only serve to put the whole industry in a state of flux that would result in a free-for-all in the price war that was sure to follow.

It soon became obvious that he had the majority of members on his side, if the nods and grunts of approval were anything to go by, let alone the spontaneous round of applause he received after his speech.

Kade's quiet but assertive argument eventually won the day for the moderates among the farming fraternity. If Tanya hadn't still been smarting from his previous comments on her appearance, she would have felt very proud of him.

There had been no time for introductions before the meeting, and she had felt many curious glances directed her way during the meeting. Now that it was over and business was out of the way, Kade's popularity was evident by the way the farmers grouped themselves around them and congratulated him on his successful contribution to the conference.

Tanya's thoughts at this time were on lines of refreshment, and she was wondering whether the hotel would provide tea for them when she suddenly found herself the centre of attention with Kade's drawled, 'Meet my partner, boys.'

That was all he said, and Tanya's indignant glance at him was met with a wicked grin that widened as one of the men, a stout man who had been most effusive in his congratulations to Kade, held out a horny hand to Tanya, but directed his remarks to Kade. 'Well, you're a sly one, I must say! Not that I blame you for keeping her out of circulation until you'd nailed her. Pleased to meet you, Mrs Player, you've got yourself a fine man there.'

Tanya's blazing eyes met Kade's amused ones accusingly. He'd done that on purpose, she thought furiously. He must have done, particularly as she had requested him to introduce her as Miss Hume.

'Spare the lady's blushes, Ted,' replied Kade, resting his blue eyes on Tanya's bright cheeks. 'Miss Hume is my working partner. Tanya, this is Ted Down, a good friend of mine.'

It was a great pity Kade didn't take his own advice, thought Tanya, fuming, certain now that his lapse had been a deliberate move to take a rise out of her.

'Beg pardon, I'm sure,' muttered the man confusedly, then gave her a hard stare from out of his protuberant brown eyes. 'Why, you must be John Hume's daughter!' he exclaimed, and gave her hand another hearty pump. 'Nice to know you're back in the fold again,' he assured her sincerely.

Things were decidedly easier after this, but no thanks to Kade, Tanya thought seethingly, and her thoughts were echoed in her eyes and glacier expression each time they rested on him. As for the social evening ahead of them, she devoutly hoped he had his own plans for entertainment and it was too bad if he hadn't. She had no intention of spending the evening in his company, even if it meant developing a sick headache soon after the start of the proceedings!

Feeling as she did, Tanya was tempted to deny herself the refreshment she had looked forward to after the close of the meeting, particularly as she learned that a table had been reserved for her and Kade in the hotel's dining room. Only the fact that she was very thirsty and knew that she would get no other refreshment until the evening made her reluctantly follow Kade's tall straight back as he led the way into the dining room after the rest of the impromptu introductions had been carried out.

Kade's arrival in the dining room was hailed by another round of greetings, this time from the feminine front, who were the wives and daughters of the farmers attending the meeting, and now waited for their menfolk to join them. The interest her arrival with Kade had aroused at the meeting was nothing to the interest Tanya was now receiving from the women who eyed her with open curiosity and made her feel very self-conscious as she took the chair that Kade held out for her when they reached their table.

'You look scared to death,' commented Kade, as he handed her a plate of fresh-looking ham sandwiches. 'I should have thought you would have got used to meeting folk,' he added casually, as he took a sandwich for himself and demolished half of it in one bite.

Of course she was used to meeting people, Tanya thought bitterly, but the circumstances had been somewhat different then, although he wouldn't have understood. His next words, however, disproved this theory.

'You weren't the centre of attention then, though, were you?' he went on casually, helping himself to another sandwich and looking pointedly at the pot of tea and the still empty cups on the tray beside it.

Tanya took the hint and poured out their tea before she answered his latest taunt at her mother. 'If you mean my mother,' she said slowly, her eyes on the cup and saucer she was holding out to him, 'she didn't relish attention either.'

'I didn't say she did,' he replied curtly, 'but she got it, all the same, didn't she?' he stated baldly.

'I suppose she did,' replied Tanya slowly, 'almost as much attention as you're getting,' she added with a glint in her eye. 'It's you they're interested in, not me.'

'Want to bet on it?' he said with a wicked grin, as he took a sip of his tea.

Tanya stared back at him coldly. 'If you mean they're interested in me because I'm with you, yes,' she answered. 'I'll accept that. If I were on my own I wouldn't have got a second glance from anyone.'

Kade sat looking at her with slightly raised brows, then his blue eyes narrowed. 'You underrate yourself, Tanya,' he said quietly. There was an inflection in his voice that made her look away swiftly. 'I said you were like your mother, remember?' he added softly.

Tanya wondered if he was trying to make amends for his earlier baiting tactics. She could think of no other reason for this compliment, if it was a compliment. Her eyes remained fixed on the tea table and she made no attempt to answer.

A plate of rich-looking pastries was thrust in front of her. 'Try one of these,' said Kade with a humorous note in his voice. 'You could do with some fattening up.'

'I'm not a prize calf!' she replied indignantly, glad to have something to complain about and bring the conversation back to normal. 'And I thought we'd agreed to leave personalities out of it?' she added acidly.

Kade gave a rueful grin at this. 'The trouble with me,' he replied airily, 'is that I have a bad memory.'

'Haven't you?' agreed Tanya sweetly. 'But I happen to have an awfully good one!' She refused the pastries.

'I hope you've brought your dancing shoes,' he said, abruptly changing the conversation. Tanya gave him a wary look. 'You'll not be given much respite once the music starts.'

She did not reply but continued to survey him with that very wary look in her eye that said more than words.

Kade gave a low chuckle and she noticed how white and even his teeth were against his deep tan. 'Don't worry,' he drawled, 'I'm not that much of a dancer. You won't find yourself short of company on or off the dance floor,' he added significantly.

A spurt of alarm made Tanya's lovely eyes widen. She didn't know these people. What on earth could she talk to them about? Her life had been so different from theirs. There was one subject that she knew that they would be interested in, and she didn't want to talk about that. She looked back at Kade who was now in the act of lighting a cigarette. 'They'd want to know all about Mother, wouldn't they? And I've no intention of discussing her with them,' she added fervently, as her now pleading eyes met his sardonic ones. 'If you're staying on for my benefit, then I'd far rather we went back,' she tacked on quickly.

'Running away again, are you?' he demanded harshly. 'Well, it's no go. We're staying.' Then he went on in a grim voice: 'Sure they're interested in the past, but they're not unmindful of their manners. These are good folk, and don't you forget it. They've had their lean times in the past the same as the rest of us. You're John Hume's daughter, and as such you'll be welcomed into the fold. Don't go all high and mighty on them, they wouldn't appreciate that.'

Tanya flushed at this bald directive. He was not only telling her to mind her manners, in the way one would tell a child to behave itself, he was also telling her that these people had not had it as easy as she had, and had had to work for their living. In other words, he was accusing her of being a snob. It wasn't like that at all and surely he must know this, she thought bitterly.

As she did not reply, he carried on: 'Just give them a chance to get to know you. You'll find you've more friends than you've ever known in the past—real friends.'

There he goes again, thought Tanya, now he was saying that she hadn't a friend in the world. Her eyes rested on her tea cup, still half full, and she pushed it away; she didn't feel thirsty any more. It hurt to concede that he was right. She hadn't any real friends of her own, they had all been her mother's friends. The only person who could be said to be close to her was Connie, but she had been away from her for a long time, and anyway that was different.

Tanya remained silent although she wanted to shout out to him that she would do exactly what she wanted to do. If she didn't want to go to the social, then she wouldn't go; she would wait in her room until he was ready to take her back to Orchard Farm. She drew in her breath sharply. What was the point? She would go, of course. He had left her no choice in the matter. First he had accused her of being a coward, now he was accusing her of being a snob, and she deserved neither of these charges.

She then recalled her planned tactic of falling in with his wishes, but it didn't seem such a good idea now. The trouble was that it didn't appear to be her show any more. Somewhere along the line this large bullying man had taken over, and there wasn't a thing she could do about it, except pretend that she was still in charge. Her small chin lifted. She was still in charge because it was she who would have the last word, if not the last laugh on this autocratic character, although nothing appeared particularly funny right then.

Kade took full note of the raised chin and the light of battle in her eyes and made his own interpretation. 'Well, I guess you'll want plenty of time to pretty-up, or whatever it is you girls do in preparation for a party. I'll call for you around seven-thirty. Okay?' he asked, favouring her with an amused grin that clearly told her that he was pleased with her.

Tanya did not trust herself to speak, but just nodded and gathered up her handbag and stood up. Kade accompanied her, but was prevented from escorting her out of the dining room by a demand for his presence at one of the tables they passed. Tanya kept going, thankful for the chance of escaping from his overbearing company.

Not for one minute had she envisaged enjoying herself, but to her surprise she did exactly that. As Kade had prophesied, she was inundated with partners for the dances, and although there did not appear to be a vast number of unattached young men, since most of the farmers were elderly and accompanied by their wives, this added to rather than depleted her enjoyment. She did not find herself having to take certain measures of avoidance from boredom as she had had to do in the past. Her mother, as Kade had intimated, had certainly kept a weather eye on her acquaintances, and the young men she had deemed suitable had also been depressingly dull.

It wasn't long before the fact sank through to Tanya that these people were genuinely trying to make her feel welcome, and she couldn't help responding to such kind gestures. The personal questions she had feared did not materialise, and because she knew that they must have wondered about her mother but had carefully avoided the subject, it made her appreciate their tact and endeared them to her more firmly than any other gesture could have done.

It was an evening of gaiety that was not marred by the fact that Kade made certain that he got his full quota of dances. Had Tanya been honest with herself she would have had to admit that her dances with Kade enhanced rather than marred the evening.

She was feminine enough to appreciate his studious attention and quite unable to stifle a little lift of pride when he led her on to the dance floor. Where the women were concerned, there was no shortage of young partners, and Tanya had noticed that Kade had made a point of dancing with these girls, ensuring that no one was left out. She also noticed that he did not dance twice with the same girl, but many times with her.

It was as if, she mused as she was dancing with him, he was determined to lay a claim to her company. She could dance with his friends, but he was the one who had brought her and the one who was escorting her home. A slight flush came to her cheeks as she acknowledged that his tactics could be misinterpreted by a watchful observer, and she wondered if he had realised this.

When he asked her if she was enjoying herself, she was able to give an affirmative answer and this time mean it. There really hadn't been any need to ask such a question, as her slight flush and sparkling eyes told their own story. 'How does it feel to be the belle of the ball?' he queried teasingly.

Tanya's eyes lost a little of their sparkle as she gave him a searching look, not sure if he was making fun of her or not. You could never tell with Kade, she thought. 'I don't know about that,' she replied quietly. 'I only know I'm enjoying myself. Let's leave it at that, shall we?'

'Guess I spoke out of turn again,' drawled Kade dolefully, but his eyes belied his tone and continued to laugh at her.

The next dance was claimed the moment she and Kade walked off the floor, and although she was tiring now Tanya did not like to refuse the elderly man whom Kade had addressed as Tom, and had introduced to her at the start of the evening. At least it would be a leisurely trot around the floor, and provide her with the much needed breathing space from the more exuberant partners she had previously danced with.

Kade decided to take a breather himself and watched Tanya dancing with old Tom Watson. 'She's sure a sight for tired eyes,' commented Ted Down, the stout man who had given Tanya a few uncomfortable moments at the start of their acquaintance by calling her Mrs Player. His eyes were on her as he spoke and as both men watched, her elderly partner stepped on the hem of a middle-aged woman's skirt as he attempted to swing his partner round to the tempo of the dance. 'Time old Tom packed in dancing,' grinned Ted, as they watched both couples stop dancing and profuse apologies offered.

They continued to watch, and saw Tanya appealing if anyone had a safety pin. On being supplied with one she knelt down and started to pin up the damaged skirt, whose hem was now exposed, making it impossible for her to carry on dancing. In spite of the woman's mild, 'Oh, it doesn't matter at all. Please don't trouble yourself,' Tanya set herself to the task with a brusque, 'No trouble. If you'll just hold still, I'm sure I can fix it.'

'Got a nice way with her, too,' went on Ted musingly. 'Nothing high and mighty about her, is there? From all accounts she's had a mighty fine education too. But blood will out,' he went on ruminatively, 'She's old John's gal, all right. Tell you what,' he added, turning to the silent Kade. 'She ain't going to be a partner in anyone's business for long, that's for sure. Not with her looks, no sir! When the word gets around you'll have all the young bloods pounding a beat to your doorstep, if I'm any judge of matters.' He nudged the still silent

Kade with his elbow. 'Mrs Saddler's got a certain gleam in her eye. What's the betting she's working out the invitation wording at this very moment? Not,' he added slowly, 'that I'd like to see the lovely lass tied to that Lance of hers. She's too good for the likes of him.'

Kade turned to face him, and for a moment his companion was surprised by the grim look on Kade's face. 'Don't start matchmaking, Ted,' he said warningly. 'There's plenty of time for that sort of caper. She's only a kid yet, and she's here to learn the business.'

It was Ted's turn to be surprised and he stared at Kade. 'She's twenty, ain't she?' he demanded. 'My Essie was just turned seventeen when I put a ring on her finger. I weren't that much older myself, come to think of it, but we made a fine pair, and never regretted it, no sir.'

Kade's lips thinned as his eyes rested on the kneeling Tanya still busy with her task. He saw the way her white-blonde hair had fallen beside her cheeks almost obscuring her intent features. 'Essie's different, Ted,' he said slowly. 'She's a country-bred girl. Tanya's had a different upbringing—and a sheltered one at that.'

His companion gave him a searching look, then his weatherbeaten face broke out in a wide grin. 'If you say so,' he replied, with an air of someone who had just made a momentous discovery and wanting to savour the knowledge.

'I do say so!' bit out Kade harshly. 'And you can take that know-all grin off your face,' he added furiously, then gave a half-shake of his head, and grinned back at Ted. 'You always were one to rush your fences, Ted, but this time you've fallen over the first hurdle. Come on, they'll be calling for the last drinks soon.'

Ted patted Kade on the back in the manner reminiscent of an elder brother sympathising with a younger one, and followed him to the bar.

Tanya was a little surprised when Kade told her that it was time they started on the return journey home. The last dance had not yet been announced and she couldn't understand his sudden rush to make tracks, as he had put it. However, she was not complaining, she was very tired in the pleasant utterly relaxed state of being that follows an exhilarating evening.

If Kade had hoped for a swift leavetaking he was disappointed. As soon as they made for the door there seemed to be a general exit of the rest of the company, and Tanya found herself shaking hands on her way out. There were calls of 'Have to have another get-together soon,' and she felt a lump in her throat at the thought that she would not be attending next year's annual conference, or indeed be able to accept any of the hinted invitations that had come from the farmers' wives for future parties.

They had almost made the door when a tall gaunt-looking woman thrust her way through the gathering around them and held out a thin heavily veined hand to Tanya. 'I shall be sending you an invitation for the twentieth,' she announced regally, 'and I won't take a refusal,' she went on, showing a set of horsy-looking teeth to soften the dictatorial order.

'Afraid you're going to be disappointed, Mrs Saddler,' drawled Kade. 'We're off to Sydney for a few days on the nineteenth for a loaders' conference. Some other time, maybe?' he added casually, and met the annoyed woman's eyes firmly.

'Very well,' Mrs Saddler muttered ungraciously.

'Some other time, then.' This was said with a certain amount of determination in her voice.

As Tanya collected her case from her room and went down to join Kade waiting in the car park for her, she thought about the strange encounter with the woman Kade had addressed as Mrs Saddler. She didn't know whether it had been her imagination or not, but she had sensed that Kade had not liked the woman, and wondered if they really were going to Sydney, or whether it was just an excuse given by Kade to get her out of the invitation, and if so, she wondered why.

When the car door was slammed behind her and Kade had got into the driving seat, she was glad that she had not bothered to change out of her evening dress and had slipped her jacket coat over her shoulders, for the evening air was chilly and she was grateful for the long folds of the dress now tucked round her legs.

Her thoughts were still hovering around Mrs Saddler, and her what now appeared to be mysterious invitation. Kade was silent, but not morose, even so, she hesitated to seek enlightenment from that quarter. A thought then struck her that made her glad that she had not asked for an explanation. The woman had probably known her mother and now sought information from Tanya. On recalling the woman's small snapping eyes and sharp pointed features, this solution seemed more than probable, and she felt a spurt of gratitude towards the still silent Kade for his intervention.

Certain that she had now solved the mystery, Tanya relaxed into a state of happy drowsiness. She wouldn't let thoughts of the future spoil her wonderful evening, and hadn't she been too hard on Kade? He had only wanted to watch out for her, after all. As for her de-

luding herself that she was in love with him—well, she
was just one of many, and that was perhaps the trouble.
It was the fashion to fall for men like Kade, but like
Linda, they all had to come to their senses some time or
other and settle for reality. Linda loved her Bill, she
thought drowsily, and there was no reason why she too
shouldn't one fine day meet the man who was destined
to stand beside her during the years to come.

Her happy musings were interrupted by Kade. 'If you
get any more invitations from that woman, turn them
down,' he said abruptly.

It took a moment for Tanya to come out of the
drowsy state and concentrate on his words. By 'that
woman' she presumed he meant Mrs Saddler, and her
interest was once again awakened. 'Why?' she asked
curiously.

'Because of her son, Lance Saddler, that's why!' he
answered curtly. 'I don't want you mixed up in his company. No decent girl would be seen out with him. He's
got an unsavoury record where women are concerned.'
He stared at the road ahead of him. 'I blame his mother
as much as anyone else,' he went on harshly. 'She didn't
deny him a thing. Worships the ground he walks on,
with the result that he's turned out to be a thoroughly
unreliable waster who doesn't intend to do a day's work
while he can wheedle money out of his mother.'

Tanya's eyebrows rose; he was certainly laying it on
strong, she thought, and again she sensed the big
brother act from Kade, but this time it didn't annoy
her. 'I gather he's crossed off your list of suitable
friends, then,' she said in a light teasing voice.

Kade glanced down at her swiftly, before he answered
in a tone that said that he wasn't amused. 'Who said I
had a list?' he barked out at her.

Tanya blinked at this unwarranted attack. She had only been joking. 'I was only joking, Kade,' she said swiftly, not realising that she had called him Kade, and not Mr Player, but Kade noticed it.

'Getting chummy now, are we?' he said sardonically. 'Am I allowed to call you Tanya now, and not Miss Hume?'

His rather cruel reminder of their earlier antagonistic attitude towards each other hurt her. So it was back to battle stations, she thought wearily, just when she thought it might be possible for her and Kade to get on. 'If you like,' she answered in a small tight voice, back to hating him for ruining the end of what had been a lovely evening.

They drove on for another mile or so, then Kade wrenched at his tie and loosened it. 'It was sure stuffy in that room,' he said quietly.

Tanya did not reply but gazed out at the road ahead. She felt rather than saw him glance at her as if seeking some comment on this, but she refused to satisfy him. Whatever she said would be wrong, so she might as well hold her tongue. She sensed that he was attempting to make some sort of apology for his bad humour and putting it down to the crowded dance room.

He needn't bother, she told herself bitterly. He had succeeded in spoiling everything for her. He must have known that she had thoroughly enjoyed herself and couldn't resist pricking her pretty balloon of memories. Her small teeth clenched together. How could he say that he wanted her to stay on, and then make life uncomfortable for her? What sort of a man was he?

She swallowed convulsively. A man who was loyal to his friends. He didn't care about her; but he had cared about her father.

There was another deep sigh from Kade as he gave her a swift glance and then looked back at the road. It was as if he had said, 'Well, I tried, didn't I?' to the heavy silence around them.

He was right, in a way, Tanya thought. He had tried, but how it must have gone against the grain. Her presence must be a thorn in his flesh. He thought of her as a society drone, and although he had made a good try at forgetting her upbringing, he invariably referred back to it, particularly if they were having an argument, or if she had annoyed him in any way.

The rest of the journey was completed in the same oppressing silence, and Tanya for one was devoutly thankful when the car swept up the drive of Orchard House.

Her relief was shortlived, however, when Kade stood beside her at the back door, and at her quick annoyed glance up at him he said casually, 'There'll be a flask of hot coffee on the kitchen table, if I know Connie.'

That was all he said, but it was enough to show Tanya that he intended to share the flask with her, whether he was welcome or not, and it would have been the latter if she had had the choice. As it was, she could do no more than follow him with lagging steps towards the kitchen, fervently wishing that she had the courage to say that she was tired and would he mind if she went straight up to bed. He would mind, of course, she told herself wearily, and he would let her know that he did in no uncertain manner.

There was also the plain fact that he intended to try and make up for his lapse of humour on the return journey, and as before, Tanya could see no reason why he should bother.

The sight of the large flask set right in the middle of the kitchen table complete with two cups and saucers and a plate of biscuits made her even more depressed, as she had hoped that for once Connie had failed in what she would consider to be her duty. Even the delicious smell of the hot coffee wafting towards her as Kade filled the two cups did not lighten her mood, and her look was hardly grateful as she accepted a cup from him.

'Biscuit?' asked Kade, as he settled himself down on one of the kitchen chairs, and raised one expressive eyebrow at her refusal.

If he made one more remark about her needing to put on weight, then she would go straight up to bed and leave him to it, she told herself grimly as she stared back at him still holding the plate out towards her. 'Well?' she demanded with a glint in her eye.

Kade's blue eyes sharpened perceptively as he met the challenge. 'I daren't say a word,' he said sardonically, as he put the plate down. 'Not even a nice one,' he added meaningfully. 'The trouble with you, Tanya, is that you're always looking for trouble, and that isn't going to be good for business.'

Tanya gasped audibly, and stared at him. Was he deliberately baiting her? she wondered, and decided that he was. She had spoilt his planned act of smoothing over her ruffled feelings and he hadn't liked that. 'No, it isn't, is it?' she replied smoothly, surprising herself with her cool answer. 'So let's face it, shall we? I'm not cut out for it.' Her last words were not quite so firm, the tiredness she had felt earlier had suddenly overtaken her. 'Can you really see me as a business woman?' she asked him wearily.

Kade's narrowed eyes rested on her flushed cheeks and her bright hair whipped in a halo round her small features by the strong breezes coming in the car window on the way back. He could see her as anything but, but he had no intention of saying so. 'You're tired,' he said abruptly, and stood up. 'It's time you hit the sack. You'll be okay.'

Tanya blinked rapidly. He wasn't going to give in, and she was too tired to argue about it now. She stood up and turned tiredly towards the door. 'If you say so,' she said in a low dispirited voice, and turned to leave. 'Goodnight,' she added indifferently.

Kade was standing by the door when she reached it. 'Is that all I get?' he said softly.

Tanya looked up at him. Here was the big brother act again, she thought dispiritedly. Now he was sorry for her, he knew she was low and was trying to comfort her, much as a big brother might have done, or her father come to that. Because he had made the gesture she could not ignore it. Tomorrow they would fight again, but it would be churlish of her to refuse to accept the peace-offering.

Accepting the gesture in the spirit that it was given, Tanya automatically lifted her face towards him and offered him her cheek in the same way as she had done with her father. She felt Kade's firm lips on her cheek, and as she would have done with her father, she turned to say another goodnight before leaving him, but he had not moved away from her.

The next moment she found herself pulled none too gently into his arms, and receiving a very unbrotherly kiss that made her senses reel. The action was too fast and too sudden for her to take evasive measures, and she just had to accept the kiss whether she liked it or not.

The shock had still not worn off when he released her, and she stood staring at him with wide eyes. Her stunned reaction caused him to take a deep breath, then swing away from her. 'I'm sorry, kid,' he said stonily. 'I guess I took more on board at that party than I usually do. No hard feelings, I hope?' he added, casually dismissing the event.

'No hard feelings,' Tanya answered, just as stonily, and this time was able to leave him.

CHAPTER SEVEN

Iᴛ was a long time that night before Tanya fell asleep. Her mind was in a turmoil and her thoughts were not inducive to sleep.

Having now absorbed the shock of Kade's hard forceful kiss, she was now left with the aftermath—an aftermath that had brought certain undesirable elements into their relationship. It was his casual 'no hard feelings' remark that was causing her most of her worry. As for his excuse of having taken too much drink—well, that was a non-starter, and although it had been a convenient excuse, he must have known that it was a pretty lame one, and that she would see through it.

Why then had he kissed her like that? She had given him no encouragement whatsoever. She turned over on her left side and bunched her pillows up under her head. So he felt sorry for her, but you didn't go about kissing folk you felt sorry for—at least not like that! It was plain that he had given way to an impulse and had immediately regretted it. His 'Sorry, kid' apology was proof enough of this. It was as if he had had to remind himself that she was totally inexperienced. Her reaction alone would have shown this, she thought.

Her smooth brow deepened into a frown. It wasn't like Kade—at least not like the Kade she thought she knew. Did she know him, she asked herself, or had she built up a completely false picture of the man who had dominated her father's business for all those years?

Hadn't her mother fallen into the same trap? Building him into a godlike figure, only to find that he had feet of clay. Had she, too, just found this out? Wasn't he just like any other man, with the same instincts and the same needs as other men?

She felt the tears gathering at the back of her eyes. She had trusted him. She had offered him her cheek and he had taken her lips. She might have expected this of any other man, but not Kade.

She closed her eyes as she felt a wave of bitter disillusionment flow over her. What right had he to order her to stay away from what he considered unsavoury types? What difference was there between him and the man he had spoken so disparagingly of in the car coming home? A tiny voice reminded her that Kade worked for his living and the other didn't, but she refused to listen to it. She was in no mood to accept the finer points of any such argument.

When she recalled his earlier disparaging remarks about his not hankering after kids, she wished she had had the presence of mind to slap his arrogant face after he had kissed her. For all his fine ideals it had not prevented him from taking advantage of her at the first opportunity offered!

There would never be another one offered, she vowed silently. To think she had been stupid enough to actually ask him to teach her the rudiments of the romantic side of life! Her soft lips twisted ironically; he had said she would regret it, hadn't he? And she did! Her lips now set in a purposeful line. Just let him make another advance on those lines and she'd let him know that she didn't hanker after older men either!

Whatever daydreaming she had done in the past

where he was concerned was now well and truly over. It had been over before their return journey back from the party, when she had admitted to herself that in thinking that she was in love with Kade she was just following the fashion. It had been different then, she told herself bitterly. She had still respected him, and still been a little in awe of him, but not now. She no longer trusted him. Her instinct to get out had been right, and Kade had known it all along, but hadn't cared how much hurt he inflicted upon her as long as he fulfilled his side of the bargain he had made with her father.

If he could fulfil his side of the bargain with so little regard for her feelings—then so could she. He could be as sarcastic as he liked, but she would not give him the satisfaction of knowing that he had riled her, even though this was not going to be easy. He had a nasty habit of getting under her skin and somehow she had to cure this tendency of hers to hit back at him. It wouldn't get her anywhere—at least nowhere that she wanted to go, she thought as she recalled a certain look in his eye whenever she had managed to score a point over him.

At breakfast the following morning, Connie wanted to know all about the get-together after the meeting, and who was there, and did Tanya meet the so-and-so family, and reeled off names.

Tanya did her best, but it was a poor best, and she knew it. Her earlier enthusiasm over her evening out had somewhat waned in the light of consequent events, and her thoughts were on the coming meeting with Kade after breakfast. She could see a miserable day ahead, with Kade seizing upon every opportunity

offered to lash out at her. He must have had some bad
moments after his slip-up last night and no doubt
would go all out to quash any romantic notions she
might be harbouring on that score.

'Well, as long as you enjoyed yourself,' said a disappointed Connie, when the fact that Tanya's thoughts
were obviously elsewhere finally penetrated through to
her. 'You'll be getting some invitations now, you wait
and see,' she promised her happily. 'No reason why you
shouldn't accept them either,' she went on half-
scoldingly. 'You could do with a few more parties, that's
a fact,' she added, as she disappeared into the kitchen
regions.

After breakfast Tanya slipped up to her room to collect the matching jacket to her dark blue tailored
pants, and frowned at its immaculate cut. It wasn't
really the sort of thing to wear on a fruit farm, but
then none of her clothes were. She needed jeans and
plain blouses, not the white and blue striped silk one
that she wore at present and that belonged to the suit.

When she was ready she gave herself a critical look
in the mirror, and saw with annoyance that her hair was
not behaving itself, and refused to stay neatly in position. She gave an exasperated sigh and on an impulse
plaited it, securing the ends with two tightly twisted
elastic bands. The result somewhat surprised her, for
her hair was not long enough to achieve the desired
neat appearance but stuck out on either side of her
head, making her look not much above sixteen.

Kade's words came to her as she stared at her reflection in the mirror. 'Kid', he called her, she thought
grimly—well, she certainly looked the part now, and
that, she told herself firmly, ought to settle any worry of

his about her nurturing any romantic notions where he was concerned.

To add to the illusion she wanted to create, she took off her jacket; the day would get much warmer later on and she would only end up carrying it around. Next she let her blouse hang loose around her waist instead of leaving it tucked under the waistband of her pants. When she had finished she stood back and surveyed the result and gave a nod of approval. She couldn't see anyone mistaking her for Kade's wife now—his daughter, maybe, she thought with grim satisfaction.

A hoot on a horn made her hastily snatch up her shoulder-bag and rush for the door. She had no intention of giving Kade a stick to beat her with that early in the morning by being late on parade!

The car door was open on her side when she reached it, as if Kade was impatient to get going, and she got in hastily thinking that it looked as if her earlier presumption of his being in a bad mood was correct.

Kade started the motor as soon as she had slammed the car door behind her, and gave her a quick odd kind of assessing look that she could not interpret, but there had been a look of amusement in his eyes before he gave his attention to the road again.

If this was so, then it must have been the hairstyle that had amused him, thought Tanya sourly, but she had no intention of giving him an opportunity of commenting upon it. She ought to have known better!

'It did upset you, didn't it?' he said in a slow amused voice. 'It proved that I was right, though, didn't it?' he added casually.

Tanya looked straight ahead of her but was unable to prevent the flush of delicate pink staining her cheeks

and was certain that he had taken full note of her discomfort. 'If you're referring to last night,' she replied
coldly, 'I'd rather forget it, if you don't mind. I'm surprised you brought it up,' she added tartly, 'I should
have thought you'd have been terrified of my over-
reacting to what was obviously meant to be a comforting action on your part.'

'Comforting?' queried Kade with a slight frown. 'Is
that how you saw it?' he asked curiously.

Tanya's eyes left the road and she looked at him.
'You felt sorry for me, didn't you?' she said bluntly. 'I'm
just telling you that I understand how you felt, but I'd
far rather you'd actually said so instead of—doing what
you did.' She hesitated on the last few words, not wanting to say 'kissed me as you did'.

To her amazement and fury Kade gave a low chuckle
as he darted a quick sideways look at her. 'Has it ever
occurred to you that I did precisely what I wanted to
do?' he asked softly, making her cheeks turn a shade
deeper pink.

'Yes!' she bit out at him, furious at his autocratic
assumption that he could do as he liked with her. 'But
I prefer to incline towards my explanation rather than
look on you as a womaniser!' Now chew on that! she
thought tartly.

She saw his brows go up at this, then to her further
fury she saw an amused smile playing round his firm
lips. 'You've a lot to learn, kitten,' he drawled madden-
ningly. 'But I'll give you ten out of ten for trying,' he
added meaningly.

It was Tanya's turn to frown. Did he mean taking the
rise out of him? She gave a slight shrug. She would
never understand him, and perhaps it was better that

way. She ought to have picked him up on the 'kitten' label, though, but all things considered it was better that he saw her as a young girl rather than a woman. Better for both of them and decidedly safer for her!

Their destination that day was the distribution centre situated on the outskirts of Hobart. It reminded Tanya of London's old Covent Garden. There was just as much activity and she found that she had to dodge out of the way of loaded trolleys being manoeuvred into position by busy porters intent on moving the various commodities handled, in the shortest possible time.

It was from here that the produce was sent directly to the shipping lines to be despatched to their ultimate destinations. With the bustle and the shouts of 'Mind your back!' Kade had to shout to make himself heard as he explained the routine carried out at this stage of the business. There was never any lull in the centre, for loaded trucks were either arriving or leaving in continuous activity.

Kade's popularity here was just as noticeable as it had been on the farm with the seasonal workers, and he was hailed on all sides as they toured the depot. Tanya came in for the same amount of curious attention as she had received at the farmers' meeting the previous day.

'Taken to guided tours now, have you?' commented one wag with a grin, as he eyed her with frank curiosity.

Kade grinned back at him. 'We'll have a little more respect from you, Jack Hailey,' he replied. 'This is John Hume's daughter, and my business partner, so mind your p's and q's.'

Tanya saw the man's eyebrows shoot up and a large hand was thrust out towards her. 'Beg pardon, miss,' he said hastily. 'Right pleased to meet you.'

As she took the proffered hand, Tanya felt a spurt of satisfaction at being addressed as 'Miss'. Her 'disguise' had obviously had the desired result and had foiled any attempt Kade might have made at her further discomfiture, as she was convinced he had done before. She was even more convinced when she caught Kade watching her with a certain look in his eye that told her that he was well aware of her thoughts and was deriving some amusement from the fact.

It was a relief to her when they moved on to the office section of the depot. For one thing it was much quieter there, and it was not necessary to shout to make oneself heard. Tanya was shown where the paper work came in, and recognised the now familiar pink export forms being processed ready for export.

As Kade went through the procedure with her, outlining every stage with studious attention to detail, she caught several envious glances darted her way by the office female staff, but mostly their attention was directed at the tall bronzed man by her side, dressed now in a blue checked shirt and grey tapered slacks. They must, she mused, look an extremely odd pair, Kade every inch a man of the world and she——? A gawky schoolgirl? she thought with some amusement, as she recalled the way her hair stuck out at odd angles on either side of her head.

'I think that's enough for this morning,' said Kade, breaking into her musings. He then thanked the head clerk for the use of the office and steered Tanya out of the offices and through the still busy depot, and out to the parking lot where he had left the car.

'I noticed that you didn't ask any questions,' he said,

as he held the car door open for her, giving her an interrogating look that warned her to be careful as to how she answered this unspoken accusation.

'I didn't need to,' she answered quietly. 'You were so explicit,' she tacked on, darting a quick glance at his profile to note his reaction to this blatant flattery.

She saw his strong jaw tighten, then relax into the familiar mocking smile. 'Determined to be a brilliant student, are you?' he drawled, as he negotiated the car out of the car park and out on to the main road.

'Isn't that what you want me to be?' she asked quickly, having a nasty feeling that he had seen through her master plan to keep him happy until she could walk out on him.

'It's what you want that matters, though, isn't it?' he shot back at her. 'And there are times when I suspect that we might not be working for the same ends,' he added significantly, and Tanya caught a glint in his blue eyes as he took a swift glance at her before concentrating on his driving.

Even if he had guessed what she was up to, there was nothing he could do about it, she told herself comfortingly, as she answered complacently, 'Well, I suppose only time will tell,' and left it at that.

To her relief he did not comment upon her ambiguous answer, and they drove for a few miles in silence. 'I've some paper work to catch up on,' Kade said, as they approached the home boundary, and Tanya's inward sigh of relief that he was going to give her the afternoon off was rudely shattered by his next words: 'You might as well give me a hand. It's management business. It's a pity you can't type. We'll have to fill in those interminable forms by hand. There's a lot of paper work connected with any business, but ours involves many side issues.'

Tanya noticed that he said 'ours' and not 'mine', and she wondered if he was taking a leaf out of her book and trying a little duplicity on his own account.

When he stopped the car outside his quarters and asked in a matter-of-fact way if she had any objection to a cold lunch, she stared at him. Was he inviting her to take lunch with him there? His mocking look and twisted grin said it all for her. He was! And his drawled, 'I promise not to bite,' made it worse for her, particularly as she knew that he was referring to what had happened the previous evening. What an irritating man he was, she thought crossly. As if she was likely to give him another chance like that.

'Besides,' he teased, lightly touching one of her pigtails with a lean forefinger, 'I've got the message!'

Tanya's slight flush acknowledged this blunt comment and her teeth were clenched together tightly as she followed his broad back towards the rear of the chalet.

The kitchen quarters were small, but adequate enough for a bachelor's establishment, Tanya thought, as she gazed around her, noting with a spurt of surprise how clean and neat everything was. Kade must be a model of perfection, she thought, as there was no sign of crockery or cutlery in sight on the well-scrubbed table. However, his next comments explained this.

'Charlie looks after the place for me. He used to work in the stables, you might remember him?'

Tanya nodded abruptly. She had a vague impression of a tall sparse man who had started work there shortly before she and her mother had left Orchard Farm. This memory was tinged with bitterness. The stables had been mainly for her mother's use since her father had not been keen on riding.

As if sensing her feelings Kade went on casually, 'We only keep two horses now, and there's not enough to keep him busy there, so he took on the job of keeping me straight.'

Tanya watched Kade open the door of the refrigerator and peer inside, but her thoughts were still on the past. She had made only one visit to the stables since her return home, and the sight of the empty stalls and the sheer inactivity of the place had saddened her, and made her wish that she could put the clock back. She had not made another visit.

She gave herself a mental shake and saw Kade bend down and take a bowl of salad out of a lower shelf, then a plate of cut ham. It was a well-stocked refrigerator, she noted, and one of the large modern models.

'Good old Charlie,' commented Kade with a satisfied smile. 'I always said he'd missed his vocation. He should have been a chef. Even Connie was surprised how he adapted to the houseboy job. I suppose,' he added thoughtfully, as he placed the bowl of salad and the plate of ham on the table and collected cutlery from a drawer beside the gleaming stainless steel sink unit, 'it makes a difference if you've had to shift for yourself as he had always done. He'd plenty of cooking practice in the past.'

He placed the cutlery on the table and then produced two plates from a wall cupboard, and inclined his head towards the table indicating that she should be seated.

As she did so, Tanya felt very self-conscious, and

vaguely wondered what on earth they would have to talk about during lunch. So far, he had kept the conversation going on mundane subjects, but how long this pleasant state of affairs would last depended entirely upon his motivation. For her part she was willing to go along with his what appeared to be recent rejuvenation of their relationship, but by experience she had found him to be a very complex character, liable to break out of his complacency when she least expected it, and always to her discredit.

With these thoughts in mind, she decided to play it cool and not say one word that might cause dissension between them. If the going became sticky, she could always ask him questions about the business as it looked as if he had expected her to do after their visit to the depot. The trouble was, she thought with slightly narrowed eyes, what aspect of the business should she choose for further enlightenment?

Her concentration on this knotty problem was broken by Kade handing her the bowl of salad. She accepted it with an absentminded air, and vaguely noticed as she held out her hand to accept it that she had a tear in the sleeve of her blouse and a thread of the fine silk material hung loose.

'You should have worn a cotton top,' commented Kade, looking at the torn thread. 'The depot's no place for fine clothes. There's too much traffic in crates.'

Tanya just nodded in silent agreement with his observation. She would have worn a cotton top had she possessed one, but she saw no reason to buy one, not when her resources were as low as they were, but she didn't suppose Kade had thought of that, and she most certainly wasn't going to tell him.

'We'll have to get you some,' commented Kade, as he held the plate of ham out to her. 'I don't suppose you possess anything in that line, do you?'

Tanya wondered if he was getting in another sly reference to her past life. 'No, I don't,' she replied quietly, and left it at that.

He helped himself to some salad and ham before he said ruminatively, 'They usually have that sort of gear on sale at the conventions. It's a gimmick, of course, and they're usually advertising something or other, but I don't suppose you'd mind that?' he asked abruptly.

Tanya's wide eyes showed her surprise at the question. He was probably telling her that she could get one cheap at such meetings, not that she would bother. In the event she played safe by shaking her head to indicate that she wouldn't mind.

'Right!' he said brusquely, as he attacked his salad, 'I'll pick you up a couple tomorrow. I've promised to look in on one of my father's conventions. He likes to feel I'm still interested even if I prefer the country life to the city one.'

There was several minutes' silence after this odd offer of his while they ate their meal. Tanya wondered if she was going to be the proud owner of a T-shirt that bore the legend 'Player's Mills' inscribed across the front—or worse still, she thought, almost choking on a small piece of ham—the name 'Player' in large capitals! And she found herself devoutly hoping that they had either sold out of the shirts before he arrived, or that he would be kept too busy to remember his threat!

Her slight cough aroused Kade's attention and he glanced at her. 'Any preference for colour?' he asked, giving her a nasty suspicion that he had gauged her thoughts to a nicety and was now hugely enjoying himself. 'For the sweater, I mean,' he added, giving a mock frown. 'At least, I suppose that's what they are. I'd better have your size, too,' he tacked on, relentlessly pursuing the subject.

Tanya was finding it exceedingly difficult to hold on to her temper. He was getting personal again; as if it mattered what colour the wretched things were! As for sizes, the usual norm was small, medium, and large— and he could take his pick since she wouldn't be wearing them anyway!

She met his feigned innocent look with a glint in her eyes. 'I'm hardly the type to fill a sweater,' she replied, taking refuge in brevity as she had a sudden vision of the voluptuous Melanie who had made a point of going in for sweaters. 'I think you'll find they're called T-shirts,' she added casually. 'As for colour, I've no real preference.'

'And size?' he persisted, his blue eyes lingering on her flushed cheeks, then moving slowly down her slight figure. 'Teenage, at a guess,' he observed in amusement.

Tanya was done with humouring him. 'Oh, sure, that figures!' she drawled, putting on a thick American accent to emphasise her feelings in the matter.

'I'd rather you didn't use slang,' he replied curtly. 'It doesn't become you,' he added harshly.

For a moment or so Tanya was too surprised to answer this cold rebuke. He had turned on the elder statesman act that made her feel an awkward fledgling—until it suited his purpose to see her as an adult, she thought bitterly. 'Sorry, Pop,' she replied, somehow managing to keep her voice light and breezy. 'I keep forgetting my place,' she added for good measure.

She felt his strong fingers grip her wrist and forcibly wrench her out of her chair, giving her no time to savour the brief look of astonishment she had caught a glimpse of before his swift reprisal, and found herself held hard against his lean strong body with one arm held in an iron hold behind her back and the other rendered completely useless by being crushed against him.

Her chin was caught in the same steely hold and she was made to look up into his blazing eyes. She knew he was going to kiss her, and that the kiss would not be a pleasant one, for it was going to be a punishment for stepping out of line. All this she knew but was powerless to prevent it.

The kiss did hurt, but Tanya's feelings suffered more than the actual physical assault on her soft lips. She was made to feel a wanton and used as such. A kiss was an intimate communication between a man and a woman. It could tell of love and tenderness and need, or it could be brutal and totally annihilating, and such was Kade's kiss. His hard lips were seeking to not only dominate her very existence but to reach through to her very being. Somewhere in that hard crushing kiss she had sensed frustration, and her shocked senses had wondered at it. Only when his lips finally released hers did she have the answer. He wanted her to grow up. He wanted to be able to treat her as a woman, in every sense of the word, and the thought terrified her. She was no match for him and never would be. She didn't know much about love, but if this was a foretaste, she could do very well without it. But it wasn't love, she thought bleakly. It was one bullying man intent on crushing all opposition and not caring who got hurt in the process.

Her shocked eyes met his hooded ones and she could sense his satisfaction at having reduced her to this state of weakness. 'You had no right to do that,' she said, in a breathless whisper that spoke of her inward turmoil. 'Don't you ever touch me again, do you hear? I'm not one of your girl-friends,' she spat out at him. 'Save your masculine demonstrations for them in future and leave me alone!'

'Then keep a rein on that tongue of yours,' he bit back at her harshly. 'You asked for all you got. Call me that again and so help me you'll get the same treatment—no matter where we are. Is that understood? I've taken a lot from you, more than from any other woman, but there's a limit, and you've overstepped it. I'll not warn you again, and I'll take reprisal any damn way I want.'

He flicked a contemptuous finger at her pigtails. 'And don't think that teenager image you're trying to dodge behind will stop me, it won't. If anything, it has the reverse effect. I told you you had a lot of growing up to do, so you can take this as the first lesson. By the time I've finished with you, you'll know you're a woman, not an adolescent masquerading as one. If you still want to clear off to Oregon when the time's up, you'll have my blessing. At least I won't be worried about letting you loose in the big wide world, because by that time you'll be able to handle any unwanted advances you'll be getting from the wolf sector.'

He studied her still partially stunned wide eyes. 'You can stop fooling yourself for a start,' he told her grimly. 'You want me to notice you. It's part and parcel of growing up. It's as well that I recognised the tactics, someone else might not have done and you'd have been in trouble, and an easy mark for the Lance Saddlers of this world.'

It took a second for Tanya to work out who he was talking about and then she had it. A wave of bitterness washed over her. He was telling her that it was all right for her to make a fool of herself over him, he was used to it, but woe betide her if she sought tuition elsewhere! She felt like shaking her head as if to clear the fog that was surrounding her senses. Surely he didn't really believe what he was saying? He was making her sound like a wild filly that needed a master's hand, and he intended to be that master! It wasn't like that at all, and he must know it, she thought bewilderedly.

When she recalled what he had said about her being an easy mark for any unsavoury character, her bewilderment turned to fury. Where did he think she had spent the last few years? In a convent? How dared he assume he could run her life for her! One minute he was telling her that she was a woman, and the next telling her he was out to protect her from the big bad world! He couldn't have it both ways!

'I'd rather make my own mistakes if you don't mind,' she bit out at him furiously. 'I've heard that you learn more that way. And what's more,' she tacked on fervently, 'I've a mind to accept Mrs Saddler's next invitation. As you said earlier, I'll do exactly what I want to do!'

'Like hell you will!' he replied savagely. 'If I find you anywhere near that ménage, what happened today will seem pleasant to what you'll get for disobeying my orders. I'll give you the hiding of your life!'

Tanya stood blinking at him, scarcely able to be-lieve her ears. He meant every word and Kade's word was law. 'Why?' she asked slowly, her eyes showing her bewilderment at his adamant declaration.

It was not really a question but a need for her to understand his reasoning behind what amounted to an ultimatum, and Kade recognised it as such. 'Because you're John Hume's daughter, that's why,' he replied harshly. 'I've still a lot of respect for that name, even if you haven't.'

There was no answer to that, Tanya thought wearily, but at least a lot of what had happened now made sense —well, a kind of sense anyway. Without realising it he was attempting to play the father role in her life. To him she was a fledgling that needed guidance and whether she wanted it or not he was set on giving her that guidance.

'Now sit down and finish your lunch,' said Kade, casually, as if nothing had happened.

Tanya gulped. Food would choke her—and as for spending the rest of the afternoon in his company—she couldn't do it! 'I'm not hungry,' she said quietly. 'I hadn't much of an appetite before, so I'll pass, thank you.' Her eyes met his squarely. 'You're not going to believe this, but I have a headache, and would like to go home.'

'To cry on Connie's shoulder?' he answered de-risively. 'Okay, run away again! Spill out your troubles to Connie, she's enough sense to put you right. We'll do the paper work tomorrow. I want you here sharp at nine. I've to be in Hobart at twelve and I want that out of the way by eleven.'

Tanya gave a curt nod at this autocratic order, only

too happy to be able to make her escape, and had to exercise a lot of self-control to prevent herself from running out of the kitchen towards freedom.

She had closed the kitchen door behind her when she heard Kade's loud and explosive, 'Hell and damnation!' shout, that made her take to her heels in flight. Only when she reached Orchard House did she feel safe from the fury that she had felt unleashed in Kade's voice.

CHAPTER EIGHT

KADE's assumption that Tanya would seek Connie out and spill out her troubles to her could not have been more off the mark. Tanya knew where Connie's allegiance lay where Kade was concerned. As for Connie 'putting her right', what was right? Was it right that he should bulldoze her into compliance with his wishes where the question of her future was concerned?

Tanya considered herself fairminded, and Kade's way of going about things was not fair. Had she not inherited her father's streak of obstinacy she would have been completely overwhelmed by him and would have walked into a future of 'Yes, Kade', or 'No, Kade', depending upon the circumstances, and spent the rest of her life eating her heart out for him. He would have expected no less of her, indeed, would take her adoration as his due. He knew the ropes too well, and that was what was so unfair.

Connie was in the vegetable garden when Tanya had arrived back, and Tanya had had to explain why she was back early. She told a little white lie on the grounds that they had got through work earlier than anticipated, and no, she didn't want any lunch, she was going to write some letters.

This was the truth, for Tanya was beginning to feel guilty about not writing to Lloyd and telling him how she was settling down. It would also, she thought, as she selected some writing paper from the study bureau, give her an opportunity of finding out if he was still of the same mind about offering her a home.

She sat down at the bureau and taking a pen she began her letter. Firstly, she brought him up to date, informing him of her father's death, and telling him that she was now working for her living, but not mentioning the conditions she was forced to work under.

When she had written part of the letter she sat back and chewed the end of the pen. She would have to be very careful not to give Lloyd the impression that she was unhappy and make him feel obliged to whisk her out of the situation she was in. She had told him that the farm now belonged to the man who had managed the business for her father, taking care to keep personalities out of it. Kade might have been a balding man of sixty with a grown-up family, for all the impression she had given on this point.

She re-read what she had written and found that it looked as if she had lost all rights to the business, and this was not quite correct, so she added another paragraph to the effect that she still had an interest in the farm, and had been offered a partnership, but had not yet made up her mind to accept it.

She sighed when she had finished that part of it. It was true that she had been offered a partnership, but not true that she had not made her mind up about accepting it. She had, and no argument Kade could produce would alter her mind.

After a few moments' debate, she decided to leave it at that. If Lloyd still wanted her to join him then he would say so when he replied to the letter. He would say something on the lines that if she decided not to accept the partnership, his offer still held good. It would also, she thought sadly, give him a chance of backing out of the promise that had been made at a time of great personal grief for both of them. If Kade were right, and Lloyd had found consolation elsewhere, then she was offering him a let-out from what could be an embarrassing situation for both of them.

As she signed the letter and addressed it, she found herself shaking her head in silent disagreement with her previous thoughts. Lloyd had loved her mother, and was not the type to seek consolation in that very private area of his life. He had been forty-five when he had met Drusilla Hume, and from all accounts, a determined bachelor. Tanya's lovely mother had changed all that—or would have done, she thought unhappily, if fate had deemed otherwise. There would be no second-best for a man like Lloyd Warren.

The rest of the day she spent in pure idleness, listening to Connie's cheerful conversation and lending a hand in the kitchen by preparing the vegetables for the evening meal.

For once, Connie made no protest, sensing her need to keep herself busy, but when she casually commented to Tanya that they ought to ask Kade over to dinner one evening and received a non-committal reply from Tanya, she did not pursue the subject.

Connie saw things the same way as Kade, Tanya thought as she shelled the peas. They were both determined that she should eventually settle down and were willing to ease up on certain matters to ensure this conclusion. That was what Kade had meant when he had said that he had taken more from her than from any other woman. Seeing that he had taken more liberties with her than any other man would have dared, Tanya felt that they were even.

The following morning she presented herself for duty sharp at nine. She had now reached the stage of wishing for a quiet existence. She was tired of emotionalism and the vagaries of Kade's moody presence, and knew that however hard she tried to remain calm and collected, she would be inwardly quaking and on edge, waiting for the next confrontation between them.

His abrupt and rather curt, 'Good, now we can get an early start', remark as he opened the door to her did nothing to ease her anxiety. He had sounded businesslike, probably to ease her fears, but she wasn't going to be taken in by that, and her wary grey-green eyes said so as they met his cool blue ones.

As the morning wore on, however, Tanya received a pleasant surprise. For the first time since that traumatic confrontation in his office, Kade had treated her much as he had done before a few home truths had been aired between them. He was polite, but not overly so, and rather distant in manner, and keen on getting the work in hand over within the shortest possible time.

While she sat beside him looking at various forms to be filled in, and listening to his instructions as to how they should be dealt with, she found herself wondering what had brought about this swift change of tactics, if it was a tactic.

Was it possible, she asked herself, that he too had had enough and like herself now sought a more peaceful existence? There was his age to consider, too. At this thought Tanya couldn't help smiling. It was as well he couldn't read her thoughts, or the truce that appeared to have been called between them would no longer exist!

When she caught Kade's steely eye upon her she instantly regretted her lapse into levity and gave the work her studious attention. The look in Kade's eye gave her a nasty feeling that he had some inkling of her thoughts, but whether this was so or not, he did not bring her to task about her lack of concentration, and for this she was very grateful.

They were on the point of finishing the paper work when the telephone rang and with a frown Kade answered it with a curt, 'Yes?'

Tanya watched as he stared ahead of him as he listened to whoever it was that was talking to him. She noticed how the dark hairs on his wrist overlapped his gold watch strap and ran partially along his strong lean hand gripping the receiver. Her gaze then travelled to his strong features and rested on those firm lips of his. Once upon a time she had had daydreams about those strong lips, and how wonderful it would be to feel them pressing on hers. She swallowed quickly. How long ago that was! Little had she known then that her dreams would come true, but not quite in the way that she had anticipated or wanted.

'Do you know a Lloyd Warren?' Kade suddenly asked her, breaking into her reverie.

Tanya blinked. 'Yes,' she replied in surprise, then gave herself a mental shake. 'Is he on the line?' she asked, and held her hand out for the receiver.

Kade ignored her outstretched hand. 'Send him over, will you, Linda?' he ordered, and put the receiver down.

Tanya stared at Kade. 'He's here?' she asked, as if unable to believe it.

Kade nodded. 'Turned up at the offices asking for you. He's on his way over here.'

'I'll go and meet him,' exclaimed Tanya, with a spark of happy anticipation in her eyes. It would be good to see Lloyd again. If she had only known he was on his way she needn't have written that letter.

Her anticipation was somewhat dampened by the fact that Kade had followed her to the door, and she felt an irrational impulse to keep him from meeting Lloyd. Her feelings were irrational, because Lloyd was a match for Kade any day, and there was no reason for her to be afraid that Kade would influence him into his way of thinking where Tanya's future was concerned. Nevertheless, the fear persisted in her thoughts, and she flung Kade a look of indignation that he chose to ignore.

The sight of the tall bronzed American as he walked towards them very nearly caused her to break down, but she bit hard on her lower lip to prevent the tears she could feel pricking at the back of her lids from escaping. A show of emotionalism was the last thing either of them would have wanted at that time.

A second later her hand was held in his large one, and being heartily shaken. Then he stood back from her and gave her a critical look. 'A mite thinner, maybe,' he summed up in his soft drawl, 'but still my favourite girl.'

Tanya gulped. He had always called her that, and memories like that did not help at that particular time. 'You look fine,' she answered quickly, recalling the last time she had seen him when grief had ravaged his rugged features. For here was the man she had known before, a man of strength and certainty. Only in his eyes could she still detect the effects of the past. Once they had twinkled with quiet humour, now they smiled at her in lazy tolerance, but it was not the same somehow.

Lloyd then gave his attention to Kade who stood behind Tanya silently watching the meeting, and Tanya was forced to introduce them to each other. 'This is Mr Player, Lloyd,' she began, and then hesitated as she realised that she would have to explain Kade's position in the firm and this was not going to be easy. 'He was Father's partner,' she added quickly, hoping that that would clarify things.

'Manager,' drawled Kade unhelpfully, as he took the hand offered to him by Lloyd. 'And now part owner,' he added slowly, giving Tanya a look that defied her to refute this salient fact.

Tanya was not going to be coerced into playing that game. She knew very well that Kade was trying to give the impression that she was the main partner, deliberately playing down the fact that he owned most of the business and she was not much more than a shareholder. 'Kade, this is Lloyd Warren. You'll remember I told you about him,' she went on firmly, refusing to allow the glint in Kade's eye to deter her. She looked back at Lloyd. 'And don't listen to him, Lloyd, when he says he's part owner.' She looked back at Kade now watching her with narrowed eyes. 'Kade *is* Orchard Farm. Father couldn't have managed without him, neither could I,' she added significantly, quite determined to be fair about it. 'He put a lot of capital into the farm, and owns the lion's share.'

She was quite pleased with herself after this clari-
fication. It was the truth, and had successfully scotched
Kade's attempt at clouding the issue by making out
that she was indispensable.

Having, as she had thought, asserted herself, and
shown that she intended to run things her way from
now on, where Lloyd was concerned anyway, she was
furious at Kade's authoritative-sounding, 'Where are
you staying? I presume this is not just a flying visit.'

Lloyd grinned. 'Well, no,' he drawled. 'I was kinda
hoping someone would put me right there. I came
through Hobart, but it's a fair distance from here...'

Tanya broke in hastily with, 'You must stay with me,
Lloyd, I won't hear of you putting up in an hotel,
and we've plenty of room,' she added happily.

Kade looked distinctly annoyed at this, and again
Tanya sensed the protector attitude coming out. As
if Lloyd was any threat to her! she thought crossly.

'Better if he puts up here,' Kade said mildly but
firmly, totally ignoring Tanya's glare at this cool intervention, and went on, 'We're within walking distance
of the house, and I dare say Connie will do us the
honours for the evening meal. That's if you're agree-
able?' he asked Lloyd, not really giving him a chance
of refusing, thought Tanya, fuming.

'Why, that's fine by me,' replied Lloyd, in happy
ignorance of the sparks flying from Tanya's eyes towards Kade.

It was then decided that Lloyd's luggage should be
collected from the offices where he had left it, having
hired a taxi to take him out to Orchard Farm.

As Tanya listened to Kade offering Lloyd the use
of a Land Rover during his stay, after Lloyd had men-

tioned the possibility of hiring a car, she found it hard to stop herself from shouting out that Lloyd was her visitor, and would Kade Player please get lost. She then remembered the convention he was supposed to be attending. 'Isn't it time you left, Kade?' she asked sweetly, then found herself flushing under his sardonic gaze.

'I suppose it is,' he drawled, 'but I'll see Lloyd settled in first. You can have your little chat with him later, but first things first.'

Only Tanya knew what he meant. She would have plenty of time in which to air her grievances to Lloyd, that was what he was saying to her, and her small chin went up in acknowledgement of this subtle thrust.

Having succeeded in making her feel like a ten-year-old child eager to seek consolation for past injustices imposed on her by her harsh tutor, Kade took Lloyd on a tour of his quarters, leaving Tanya to cool her heels in the small study where they had been working. Her temper could have done with a little cooling too, and she was much too incensed to realise that Lloyd's arrival could prove to be a heaven-sent opportunity for her.

However, when her temper had cooled, and she was able to think a little more rationally, she was able to appreciate this fact. She not only appreciated it but revelled in it! Her moody grey-green eyes now held a spark of anticipation in them and she was able to meet Kade's narrowed gaze with a limpid look of guileless innocence that quite took his mind off whatever he had been telling Lloyd when they returned to join her.

His casual 'See you at dinner,' as Tanya and Lloyd

left the chalet, brought on a relapse where Tanya's temper was concerned. He meant to spend the evening with them, that much was clear—and every evening, if she knew Kade. He was not likely to miss the chance of spiking her guns and ramming home the fact that she belonged at Orchard Farm. It didn't matter to him whether she was happy or not. He had an obligation to fulfil where she was concerned and meant to carry it out.

Lloyd's comment of, 'That's a nice guy, Tanya,' as they walked towards Orchard House, was not exactly soothing to her ruffled feelings, but she managed to give a placid, 'Yes,' in reply. Kade was a nice guy providing you didn't oppose his wishes, she thought ironically, and the day might come when Lloyd found this out for himself.

'You said Kade was your father's partner,' Lloyd said as they neared the house. 'Does that mean that your father's now retired?' he asked.

Tanya gave a start. He didn't know that her father had died, and it was her fault for not writing and telling him. She told him what had happened, and apologised for not writing before. 'There's a letter in the post for you,' she said, 'but of course you won't get it now until you get back.'

Lloyd's arm came around her slim shoulders in a sympathetic gesture. 'That was a rotten homecoming for you,' he said quietly. 'I only wish I'd known before. I guess you could have done with some help then.' He was silent for a few seconds as they walked round to the back quarters of the house. 'I guess Kade's presence helped, though,' he said half to himself. 'I'm kinda glad he was around.'

Tanya's soft lips clamped together tightly. Little did he know just how much help she had received from Kade at that time, or the reason behind his lack of understanding. He was never to know that, she thought sadly. Losing the only woman he had ever loved was bad enough, without adding the unhappiness of the past to his knowledge.

If it ever came out, and heaven forbid that it did, Lloyd would have an entirely different outlook where Kade was concerned. As Kade had said bitterly, her father could never be sure that he hadn't encouraged her mother to make a fool of herself over him. She knew that Lloyd's feelings would be exactly the same, and jealousy alone would colour his judgment whether it was true or not.

As Tanya had surmised, Connie was in the kitchen preparing Tanya's lunch as she knew she was finishing early, and the introductions were duly carried out. When Tanya told Connie that Lloyd would be staying with Kade but that they would be having dinner there each evening, Connie's normally placid expression broke into a smile of satisfaction. As she told Lloyd with a note of happy anticipation in her voice, 'Don't get many visitors these days, and not much chance of doing some fancy cooking.'

'What she means is,' said Tanya with a smile of toleration in her eyes as she looked at Connie, 'that I'm not much of a gourmet where food's concerned, and now she can show off her culinary talent.'

'Oh, go along with you!' exclaimed Connie with a faraway look in her eye, already planning the evening meal in her mind. 'Kade doesn't like it too late,' she muttered, 'so we'll make it seven-thirty.'

It was infuriating, thought Tanya, how even the mealtimes had to be fixed to accommodate Kade. 'I hope that's all right with you?' she asked Lloyd in an attempt to show Connie that Lloyd was the guest, not Kade.

'That suits me fine,' replied Lloyd, favouring Connie with a wide grin. 'My views are the same as Kade's. I guess, like me, he sometimes likes to catch up on his paper work in the evenings, and late dinners knock a hole in the evening.'

If Lloyd had been out to please Connie, he couldn't have chosen a better way than to agree with Kade's views, and Connie's answering smile proved this. Tanya knew that she would have her work cut out to put a dent in Kade's popularity stakes. She looked at Connie, now ascertaining Lloyd's likes and dislikes in the food line, and discovering he possessed no particular fads, he went up in Connie's esteem and joined Kade on that high pedestal that up until now she had reserved for Kade alone.

As there were now two for lunch, Connie asked Tanya if she would take Lloyd through to the lounge and provide him with a sherry while she laid the table in the dining room for their lunch.

Connie was definitely impressed by Lloyd, Tanya mused, as she carried out her orders, for usually she ate her meals with Connie in the kitchen, the dining room being reserved for evening meals only when company was expected.

It wasn't only the fact that Lloyd had expressed his approval of Kade's views. It was more than that, she thought, as she handed Lloyd a glass of sherry. Anyone could have expressed the same sentiments, but

Connie was not so easily impressed. Tanya had noted the way her sharp eyes had done their own summing up of the tall American, and knew that he came out on the credit side of Connie's theoretical balance sheet.

'I suppose I ought to have let you know I was coming,' he began apologetically as Tanya picked up her glass of sherry and sat down beside him on the chaise-longue. 'There wasn't all that time, though,' he went on. 'I just made up my mind on the spur of the moment, and here I am.'

Tanya smiled at him. 'I should have written,' she said. 'It's odd, really. To think I was writing to you only yesterday, and here you are! And I'm so pleased to see you, Lloyd,' she said mistily. 'I'm only hoping you can stay long enough for me to show you around. I'm sure Kade will understand if I take a vacation,' she added, privately thinking that he couldn't very well refuse her request. The only snag being that he might take it upon himself to do the 'showing around', even though it was Tanya that Lloyd had come to visit.

'I guess I can spare a few weeks,' he replied with that same tolerant smile that somehow hurt her because she remembered how it was before. Then he was serious again. 'Of course I'm staying,' he said firmly. 'I want to find out how things are with you. From what I've learnt so far, the situation has changed from what you expected to find when you returned home.'

Tanya sipped her sherry slowly. She knew she had to be very careful here. Whatever she told Lloyd might inadvertently be passed on to Kade, for Lloyd was going to see a lot of Kade in the next few weeks. Kade was never slow on the uptake and it wouldn't be long before he gave Lloyd his version of the differences between them. She could almost hear him saying to Lloyd, 'She needs time to settle down, so don't encourage her to move on,'—or words to that effect, she thought shrewdly, and Lloyd would listen to Kade, and her chance would be lost.

Her slim forefinger tapped the rim of her glass as she replied slowly, 'That's true enough. But remember that I didn't have much to do with the business side of the firm before. Father always dropped that end of affairs whenever I visited. It's only recently that I've been given an insight into that side of it.' She gave Lloyd a wry smile. 'I don't really know what I expected when I returned. The fact that Father——' she gave a light sigh. 'Well, one never expects that sort of thing, and of course it threw me. Kade,' she said carefully, 'tried to help by throwing me into the business, but the bald fact that it's his business now and not mine makes me feel an encumbrance on his goodwill.' She swallowed here. Goodwill was hardly the word, but she was determined not to give Kade any cause to fight her on this point.

'There's also the fact that he promised my father that he would watch out for me, and he's got a bit of a thing about it.' She gave a light shrug. 'Oh, he means well, I know, but it still makes me feel a bit awkward about things. But I suppose it will all settle down,' she ended lamely, realising a little too late that in spite of her determination to give Lloyd the chance of backing out of his offer to give her a home, she had done exactly the opposite, and he must now feel compelled to honour his pledge.

'And if it doesn't?' queried Lloyd, his earnest brown

eyes searching her grey-green ones. 'Will you promise me that you'll accept my offer of a home? That's the reason why I've come, Tanya. I got to remembering how it was when we last saw each other, and wasn't too sure that I'd got through to you. I guess I wasn't too coherent myself at that time. When I didn't hear from you I kept wondering how you were faring, and decided to take a little action, and I'm glad I did,' he ended quietly.

Tanya felt a surge of gratitude flow through her. She didn't deserve such a good friend, especially when she had practically forced him to make the offer. If she had been in any way doubtful of his sincerity, she would have found a way of refusing the offer without hurting his feelings, but she did not attempt any such gambit. She needed a bolthole, and Lloyd wanted to look after her.

There would be time enough in the future to look again at what life might hold in store for her. What that future contained she had no idea, she only knew that there was nothing but unhappiness for her at Orchard Farm—or at best, a happiness tinged with bitter sweetness, because she would go on loving Kade. He had once said that she had tried to make him notice her as a woman. In actual fact, it was the other way around. She had tried her best to keep their relationship on a business footing, but it hadn't worked; Kade had seen to that.

When she recalled the look of triumph in his hooded eyes when he had finished punishing her the previous day, she felt a wave of hopelessness wash over her, and her fingers clenched round her glass as she replied to the watchful Lloyd, 'I promise to come to you when

I've fulfilled my obligation to Kade.' She then told him about her agreement to stay on for six months. 'I'm not making a very good business woman,' she said quietly. 'But at least I can say I tried. And really,' she added thoughtfully, 'I think that's all Kade asks of me—to give it a try.'

In a way it was the truth, she thought afterwards. Kade wanted nothing more from her than that she should comply with his wishes on this matter. It was the method that he was using to gain her compliance that had frightened her.

CHAPTER NINE

Now that the question of her future was definitely settled in her mind, Tanya was able to concentrate on other matters, such as showing Lloyd around her home state, for this was his first visit to Tasmania.

Her worries that Kade might prove a trifle awkward, and insist on accompanying them on their sightseeing tours, proved to be unfounded, for no such suggestion was made at dinner that evening when the plan was discussed.

It took a little while for the fact to sink into the amazed Tanya that Kade was actually in favour of the proposal, even suggesting certain places of interest that they could visit, and went so far as to offer to provide Lloyd with a detailed map of the areas to be visited.

This state of affairs was extremely puzzling to her. She wondered just how long he intended to stand on the sidelines. It was not like the Kade she had come to know during the last few weeks of their stormy relationship, and she couldn't help wondering what was behind his complacent agreement to her removal from the work scene.

It could have been that he was trying to impress upon Lloyd the fact that she was free to do as she wished. He knew who Lloyd was, and must have worked out the reason behind his visit. Her bemused gaze lingered first on Kade and then on Lloyd, as she listened to them expounding on the intricacies of load-

ing charges, a side issue that affected both men, although one was a fruit farmer and the other a cattle-
man.

Kade ought to have taken umbrage at Lloyd's presence on the scene, not to mention why he had decided
to make the sudden visit, but here they were in complete accordance with one another as though they had
known each other for years.

Her gaze lingered on Lloyd, who at that moment
was nodding in agreement with something that Kade
had said, and she noticed a touch of silver at the side of
his brown hair that lent him an air of seniority, and
brought back memories of her father. Not that Lloyd
and her father had anything in common. Her father
might have had a stubborn streak in him, but he had
been a quiet man who rarely disclosed his thoughts.

'Try some of that cream cheese on a biscuit,' urged
Connie, breaking into Tanya's reverie. 'You didn't eat
much,' she complained, as she put the coffee tray down
on the table beside her.

Tanya looked up at Connie resplendent in her best
black and white dress, and wearing an air of satisfied
bustle about her. She could not say the same of the
men's appetite, Tanya thought with an inward smile as
she recalled the way they had done justice to her cooking, and their complimentary remarks when she had
cleared the first course had left her in no doubt of
their appreciation. Lloyd had added the crowning
touch by asking her to provide him with her recipe
for the chicken chasseur, saying it was the finest he had
ever tasted.

Not wanting to put a damper on Connie's culinary
triumph, Tanya complied with her request, although
she had had sufficient to eat.

When Connie had served the coffee and returned to the kitchen quarters, Tanya went back to her musings and this time concentrated her thoughts on Kade.

His dark blue business suit and cream shirt with matching tie looked as if he had dressed for dinner, but Tanya rather suspected that it was the suit that he had worn at the convention and that he had not bothered to change back into his casual wear. She could not see him making an effort to impress anyone, it wasn't in character, although it could be argued that Lloyd's immaculate dark grey pinstripe might have had something to do with it, but Tanya doubted it.

Her silent assessment of the two men went on as they continued to discuss various aspects of their working areas. She was content to sit and listen to them. Lloyd's rather soft intonations were just as compelling to listen to as were Kade's deep authoritative-sounding comments.

They were very much alike, Tanya thought, for each played a leading role in their respective domains. If it came to a direct clash between them Tanya would have found it difficult to select a winner, for they were both instinctive fighters to whom defeat was not to be contemplated.

As these thoughts went through her mind her eyes rested on Kade's strong clean-cut features. Had he sensed that Lloyd would be a worthy opponent should hostilities ever break out between them? Tanya was certain that he had, for in spite of their attitude of bonhomie towards each other, she had sensed a certain wariness between them as if they were circling around each other and assessing one another.

It was not unlike the law of the jungle—caution first, then attack! Tanya gave herself a mental shake at this thought. What on earth made her think that? Had Kade's calm acceptance of Lloyd's presence, and his almost eager agreement that she should absent herself from the business scene and entertain Lloyd, made her conjure up a situation that did not exist?

After another moment's thought she had to admit that this was a possibility. Womanlike, she had felt a little piqued at Kade's refusal to adopt an aggressive attitude towards the man who was intent on claiming responsibility for her future—a future that had nothing to do with Orchard Farm.

She sighed inwardly. It was all very strange and she wished she had the answers.

Tanya was to find that Kade's seemingly strange behaviour got stranger as time went on. The proposed trips were carried out with Lloyd armed with the maps Kade had provided, driving them to their destinations. Not once did Kade attempt to join them, not even at the weekends when he was free from work.

Only at the dinners in the evenings did he put in an appearance, and Tanya wondered why he bothered to make a point of this as he seemed determined to stay out of the picture and give Lloyd free access to Tanya's company.

The dinners were pleasant enough, with Lloyd commenting on the day's sightseeing and Kade listening with studious tolerance at Lloyd's appreciative remarks on the natural beauties of Australia's smallest state.

Lloyd did not, Tanya noticed with gratitude, expound on similar wonders in his own country, or attempt to underrate the scenic splendours by comparison to the wonders of his native land, although he had once said to her how much he was looking forward to showing her around the States, but this was not in any way a boastful statement.

It was after the men had left for Kade's quarters that Tanya felt a sense of loss, and she didn't know why since she would be seeing Lloyd the following morning, and Kade in the evening.

This sense of loss became more pronounced as the days slipped by and soon Tanya was engulfed by it. It had stolen into her senses as stealthily as a thief would steal into a house he was about to burgle. It invaded her heart as she stood beside Lloyd and looked out from Pulpit Rock across the valley of the Derwent. It haunted her as she gazed down into a deep ravine through which a magnificent waterfall plunged down into the green depth of the forest below.

It was there again that day, when they visited the Russell Falls in the Mount Field National Park, one of the seven of Tasmania's National Parks, the Russell Falls holding pride of place in the state's many waterfalls.

The sheer mystic wonder of the glades surrounding the falls through which the water cascaded down, rushing over the rocks and past the bright green foliage of the ferns framing the banks and threatening the very existence of the tall trees that stood in its path as it rushed over the top of the falls, only served to increase her unhappiness.

In the midst of all this beauty with the rays of the sun penetrating through the forest above the falls and giving a kaleidoscope of brilliant colours, enhancing the falls with a rainbow-tinted effect, Tanya felt utterly bereft.

It was not the fact that she had decided to leave her home and turn her back on the past. It was more than that; Kade should have been there, she thought sadly. It should have been he who stood beside her, not Lloyd. It ought to have been Kade who had stood beside her in the rain forests, marvelling at the wonders of nature, and Kade who should have walked up the track to the Cradle Mountain with her, smiling with affectionate tolerance as she enthused in delight on the flora and fauna around them. The ache in her heart had continually acknowledged this and had given her the answer to her sadness.

It was useless telling herself that she would get over him. He had bludgeoned his way into her heart, and she sorely missed his dictatorial ways and bullying tactics.

Without his presence the days became static, not unlike the uneasy calm before a storm, only the storm would never come. They were dull days that lacked the essential ingredient for happiness.

Tanya knew that she was getting a preview of what life would be like without Kade, and she didn't like it at all. Telling herself that it would be a good miss wasn't going to work either; her heart knew different.

At dinner that evening she made a point of surreptitiously studying Kade, in an effort to find out whether he missed her as much as she missed him. It was a disappointing survey, since she could not determine any difference in his manner towards her, and he treated her in the same convivial way that he had adopted since Lloyd's arrival, stressing the fact, it seemed to Tanya, that they were only business partners and she was being afforded the due respect that such a position called for.

It was so uncharacteristic of Kade that she was forced to seek the purpose behind his changed attitude towards her, even though she was very much afraid she knew what it was.

If she were right, then the answer would raise her to the heavens, if wrong, cast her into the deepest gloom. Either way, there was nothing she could do about it. Her rise to the heavens would be of brief duration and leave her yearning for what could never be.

Did Kade love her? Her breath caught in her throat at the very thought—it was hardly credible—and yet she had felt his eyes rest on her on several unguarded occasions when she had been talking to Lloyd. It was nothing she could pin down, just an inward conviction that their relationship had taken on a new meaning. Just as the conviction was there, so also was another heartrending thought that followed in its train. If he did love her, he was never going to say so. He would do his level best never to let her know.

This deduction was strengthened by the recollection of what he had said earlier on in their stormy relationship, that he didn't hanker after kids. His pride wouldn't allow him to go back on that statement, she thought miserably. There was another poignant fact to consider, too, and that was that he had decided to let her go, and would not enforce the six-month time limit. He knew that Lloyd was wholly dependable and would have no qualms of conscience in relinquishing her to his care.

As much as Tanya tried to believe in this theory, she couldn't bring herself to trust her deductions. It could all be daydreaming on her part and in a way she desperately hoped it was. You could get over daydreams, she could look back on this point in time and tell herself it had all been wishful thinking, give a little sigh and get on with life again, and put it all down to the painful yet wonderful experience of first love.

Anything was better than to actually know that Kade loved her but had deliberately sent her away. She gave a slight shiver; she didn't think she could bear that.

'Say, you haven't caught a chill, have you?' queried Lloyd, giving her an anxious look. 'It was a bit chilly on that top track this morning.'

Tanya managed to come out of her unhappy theorising in time to answer with a crooked grin, 'I sincerely hope not. It's all your fault if I have,' she added, managing to inject a note of teasing in her voice, anxious not to let Lloyd or Kade know where her thoughts had taken her. She turned to Kade, watching her with that now familiar guarded look in his eyes. 'I didn't think I could make the top and tried to dodge out of the exercise, but Lloyd wasn't having any. As usual he was right, and I'm glad I went. It was a wonderful experience.'

If Tanya's mind had wandered in other directions before this small dialogue had taken place, it was plain that Kade's thoughts had taken a similar turn, for she received a hard stare from him, a look that said more than words, and she knew that he was telling her that if he'd suggested such a walk, she would have dug her heels in and refused to budge, but she had listened to Lloyd.

She had never questioned this ability of hers to decode Kade's silent messages to her, and in this she was closer to him than she realised. Such communications

were a rare and wonderful phenomenon, but she
accepted them as a kind of feminine intuition, not
attempting to see them as anything else.

It was only later that she realised that such a relationship could bring more heartache, particularly
when the silent messages were never spoken but remained tantalisingly out of reach and therefore un-
confirmed.

A fortnight later Tanya had to steel herself against
the knowledge that Lloyd would ask her to go back
with him at the end of his stay. When he did so, she
knew that she would have to say yes. She was sure that
he had talked it over with Kade and must have received his agreement for the proposed move, although
he said nothing of this when he made the suggestion.

'Come and try it out, anyway,' he had urged her a
week before his departure. 'You said yourself that you
were not cut out for the business life.' Then his face
had sobered. 'I guess I know you well enough to know
that you're not happy here, and I'd like the chance of
making those big eyes of yours start laughing again,
like they used to.'

Tanya looked away as he said this. Had her eyes
ever laughed? She couldn't remember. She certainly
couldn't visualise them doing so in the future. It would
be a very long time before she could envisage such a
state existing.

At dinner that evening Lloyd told Kade that he had
managed to persuade Tanya to return to the States
with him. To give Kade his due, he did not attempt
to look surprised, just gave a curt nod that said a lot
more to Tanya's watching eyes than any words would
have done.

In all probability he had put Lloyd up to it, she thought despondently. There wouldn't be another chance like this to get her out of his hair. Lloyd's arrival must have been a heaven-sent opportunity and one that was not going to be missed.

It was pride alone that made Tanya just that bit more attentive to Lloyd and to listen to what she hoped was an eager ear while he outlined their travelling arrangements. She somehow managed to smile at Kade and murmur something about how she hoped he could get along without her vast business acumen. Her smile was not returned, but she was past caring. If he could throw her out like that, wild horses wouldn't drag out the fact that she loved him.

Lloyd gave them the opportunity to talk things over by murmuring something about paying his compliments to the cook and went in search of Connie, leaving Tanya alone with Kade.

Tanya felt unable to look at Kade and stared down at her hands twisted in her lap. She desperately wished she could find some way of getting back at him. Even if she had wanted to change her mind about going, he was giving her no choice in the matter. 'It could have worked out,' she said in a low bitter voice.

'No way!' was Kade's curt answer, and as usual this abrupt terse answer held a wealth of meaning to her; he had no need to say more.

'We could start again, and this time become friends,' she said hesitantly, giving him one last chance to reprieve her from the situation he was pushing her into.

Kade's harsh laugh in reply made her want to hold her hands over her ears, it was so derisive. 'Not you and me,' he said harshly. 'There'd be only one way out,' he added adamantly, and at her swift flush and half negative shake of her head he went on ruthlessly, 'You know what I'm talking about, so don't pretend you don't. You and I know each other a little too well for that. What I said before still goes—I don't tangle with inexperienced youngsters.'

It was brutal, and Tanya's wide shocked eyes proved that if he had wanted to hurt her he had succeeded. Not only had he refused to consider her appeal, but he had managed to make her feel gauche and somehow pathetic.

A wave of fury swept over her. She had done nothing to deserve this. What had happened had been entirely at his instigation, not hers. 'A pity,' she drawled softly, managing to inject a note of derision into her voice. 'Just when things were getting interesting. Who's the coward now?' she asked challengingly, and gave an emphasised sigh. 'Still, I'm sure I shall put your training to good use. I'm quite looking forward to it,' she added lightly. 'You're right about inexperienced youngsters—they're boring, aren't they? I've gone off them, too. It's the older man for me from now on. You've taught me that much.'

She saw Kade's hands clench and knew that he was having trouble in keeping them off her. 'Want to shake me?' she asked sweetly. 'Or punish me as you did before? Well, that will be Lloyd's role from now on. It will be interesting to see what line he takes whenever I blot my copybook,' she ended conversationally.

Kade had turned away from her and stood staring out of the dining room window, but at these words he whirled round to face her. 'Don't bring Lloyd into this,' he said harshly, with blazing eyes. 'He's old enough to be your father!'

Tanya gave a nonchalant shrug. 'That might be just what I'm looking for,' she said offhandedly. 'You know the old saying about the father figure.' Her eyes clashed with Kade's furious ones. 'At least I expect him to have the courage of his convictions and not duck out from under,' she added bitterly.

'Is that what you think I'm doing?' Kade demanded harshly.

Her clear eyes remained fixed on his as she answered slowly, 'I don't know. I suppose I'll never know, so it doesn't matter, does it?'

It was then that Lloyd joined them, and if he noticed a certain amount of tension in the air, he made no comment, but just asked Kade if he was ready to turn in.

CHAPTER TEN

The day before Tanya's departure she received an early phone call from Kade, asking her if she would leave the afternoon free as they had some business to settle. Lloyd, she was told, had been asked to see that they got back from the proposed trip to Hobart shortly after lunch.

The fact that Lloyd had previously mentioned making the trip a morning visit, as he wanted to leave Tanya plenty of time in which to complete her packing, did not lessen her indignation at Kade's high-handed presumption that they were completely at his disposal. He had had ample time to work out her share of the business, and it surely didn't necessitate a long discussion.

When she had got over her indignation, she wondered whether Lloyd was expected to be present, but Kade had said nothing about Lloyd attending, and that meant that she would have to go it alone. That was precisely how she saw it—as just one more skirmish in the war of battered emotions—hers, that was, not Kade's.

However, there was one small consolation, and that was that as her share in the property was so small, it ought not to take long. She decided not to argue on any point but to just accept whatever he offered her, and knowing Kade, she suspected it would be a little higher than the going rate. It was worth it to him, she thought wearily, his bonus being her removal from the scene.

After a night of fitful sleep and deep retrospect, she had come to the conclusion that in Kade's eyes she was just as he had said she was—a fledgling on the point of trying out its wings. He had been brutal because he had had to be. He had seen no other way to handle it. He must have had some bad moments when he had allowed her taunts to get under his skin and had re-acted in the same way as any other red-blooded man would have done.

As he had so bluntly put it, there was only one way out of such a relationship. She attracted him, that much was certain, but that was all there was to it. He didn't love her, and despised himself for giving way to what was purely an interested male's reaction to the age-old instincts of courtship.

Tanya had wondered what would have happened if they had met in any other circumstances but the one they had found themselves in; or if she had been any-one else but John Hume's daughter, but she was Tanya Hume, and would remain so in his eyes, come what may. The rest was pure conjecture, and for all she knew she would have ended up on the crossed out list of his former girl-friends, and spent her time hoping for a phone call that would never come.

In a way he had saved her from this indignity, and she ought to be grateful for this at least, but somehow she wasn't. As Kade had despised himself for his weak-ness, so too did she despise herself for her presumptu-ous daydreams that she felt Kade had encouraged, in spite of his gallant stand to protect her interests. It

wasn't only her interests, though; his stiffnecked pride
had governed most of his actions, and would continue
to do so.

If she loved Kade, then she was a fool, and deserved
a fool's reward, and perhaps she was already receiving it!

Having come to this conclusion, Tanya was quite
able to deal with Connie who had been unable to
accept the bald fact that she was leaving with Lloyd
the following day, and intended to stay in the States.

'Of all the ridiculous ideas,' she grumbled again, as
she put Tanya's breakfast down in front of her. 'Going
off with a stranger. It's not right! What's Kade thinking of letting you do a thing like that? That's what I
want to know!'

'Lloyd isn't a stranger to me, Connie,' Tanya said
indignantly.

'I'm not saying he isn't a gentleman,' replied Connie,
'but he's not family,' she insisted stubbornly.

'Well, Kade's not family either,' retorted Tanya
dryly.

'He's as near family as you're ever likely to get,'
Connie answered with a mulish light in her eyes.
'You've had this tomfool idea ever since you heard
that story about your mother, haven't you?' she demanded. 'You haven't given Kade a chance since then.'
She sat down opposite Tanya and caught one of her
hands in her work-roughened ones. 'Forget all this
foolishness, Tanya. Stay where you belong,' she urged
her. 'You've just got off on the wrong foot with Kade,
and he's doing his best for you. I know Mr Warren's a
good man, and if there wasn't anywhere else for you
to go then he'd be the best person to look after you,

but this is your home, and this is where you belong,'
she ended firmly.

Tanya eyed the earnest Connie. What would she
say if she knew the truth? she wondered. There simply
wasn't anywhere else for her to go, her champion Kade
had seen to that.

Connie took her silence as hesitation and swiftly
added another rider to her plea. 'Go and tell Kade
you're staying on. You owe him that much for what
he did for your father.'

For a moment Tanya came very near to telling Connie the truth, but she couldn't bring herself to do it.
Connie had had some shocks in her time—and all concerned Tanya's family; she could at least spare her this
one. It would be no use telling her part of the story,
for no matter how it was told, it all ended in the same
emotional mess as before. It was a case of history repeating itself—first her mother, then Tanya. If Kade
was family, then he could only be described as the
black sheep! As far as Tanya was concerned he was
poison ivy! The sooner she got him out of her system
the better!

She looked back at Connie still watching her with
a hopeful look in her eye, and said gently, 'Nothing's
definitely settled. Lloyd asked me to give it a try, but
if it doesn't work out, then I'll be back,' she added
softly, hating herself for the lie, but she was willing to
tell a few more if it meant sparing Connie. 'And I did
try to fit in, Connie, but I found I made a poor business woman,' she tacked on swiftly before Connie
could interrupt. She gave her a small smile. 'To be
honest, I think Kade is relieved about the whole thing.

He didn't take much to my trotting behind him trying
to look intelligent.'

Connie gave her a hard searching stare. 'If that's
what you think, then you don't know Kade,' she answered firmly.

The sound of a car's tires swishing up the drive announced the arrival of Lloyd to take her to Hobart,
and with a sigh of thankfulness Tanya was able to
leave Connie to her gloomy ruminations.

At least Lloyd was cheerful, she thought as she left
the house. She badly needed some cheering up, and
was looking forward to a morning spent in his company, as she was getting tired of gloom and despond-
ency.

A little later, however, Tanya was dismayed to find
that Lloyd, too, seemed to be immersed in an unusually
sober mood, and was more reticent than she had ever
known him to be. A horrible thought that he was beginning to regret his offer seeped through her and she
found herself hoping that Kade's settlement would be
big enough for her to take off on her own. Enough,
anyway, to give her a start somewhere. Sydney, maybe,
she thought, as her mind raced on, but that would
come after her visit to Oregon. Lloyd was not likely
to cancel that at this late hour, she reasoned. So it
would be up to her to bow gracefully out of the picture after what might be termed a reasonable period of
time.

The visit to Hobart was more in the nature of a
shopping tour than a sightseeing one. Lloyd had suggested as much the previous day, mentioning that if
there was anything Tanya needed they could purchase
it then.

Tanya was sure he had a few ideas of his own on what he had called 'a shopping spree', and this included buying her a 'little something' that knowing Lloyd was bound to be prohibitively expensive. Tanya was determined to prevent any such gesture, and to this end suggested that they visit one of the State museums that housed relics of Australia's historic past and was bound to be of immense interest to the visitor.

At Lloyd's reply that he wasn't in the mood for a history lesson Tanya stared at him with raised brows, making him add with an apologetic grin, 'Guess I've a touch of indigestion. I'd rather we took it easy today. We'll have a coffee in that place for a start,' he said, indicating with a nod of his head a large restaurant opposite where they were parked.

Tanya's thoughts were hectic as he guided her to a table near a large bay window in the restaurant. She was certain he had had a change of mind where she was concerned, and wasn't finding it easy going explaining the position to her.

Well, she would make it easy for him, she thought stoutly. She would broach the subject herself and save him the embarrassment of bringing it up.

Kade had something to do with this, she was sure, but it didn't add up. Of all people he had a legitimate reason for wanting her off the scene and would hardly be likely to put a spoke in the wheel at this late stage.

It was when she remembered her last conversation —or rather skirmish—with Kade that a little light was thrown on the subject.

He must have warned Lloyd against her developing what she had termed a 'father figure complex' where he was concerned. A slight flush stained her cheeks. Poor Lloyd! no wonder he was worried!

As soon as their coffee had been brought to them and the waitress had retired to serve another customer Tanya, unable to bear the suspense, said quickly, 'You've had second thoughts about taking me back with you, haven't you, Lloyd?'

Lloyd's eyebrows shot up at this and he stared at Tanya's earnest features. 'Now where did you get that idea from?' he demanded in a surprised voice.

Having made the initial approach Tanya had no intention of giving up now. He had certainly looked amazed at the question, but he might have been playing for time.

She played with the spoon in her saucer, seeking the right words to convey her feelings to him. She wanted to tell him that she understood, and that she didn't mind. She was looking forward to standing on her own two feet. It had to be convincing, for her sake as well as Lloyd's.

'You're coming home with me,' said Lloyd firmly, breaking into her careful rehearsal of what she would say. 'I'm not taking no for an answer,' he went on quietly. 'I guess you need time to sort yourself out, and I'm going to make sure you get that time.'

Tanya's eyes widened as she digested this. Time for what? she thought bewilderedly. Then a thought struck her that made her drop the spoon into her saucer with a clatter. Kade hadn't—he couldn't! She swallowed hard. If he had told Lloyd the real reason why it was better for all concerned that she leave Orchard Farm, she would hate him for all eternity! A sort of a man-to-man confession, she could almost hear it!

Warning Lloyd at the same time that she might very well transfer her unwanted attentions to him!

She continued to stare back at Lloyd. He must have believed him, she thought wretchedly. Why else would she need time to, as he had put it, 'sort herself out'?

Lloyd put a large hand on her small one. 'Look, Tanya, I've no wish to pry into your personal life,' he said slowly, 'but I'd like to know just what goes between you and Kade.'

Tanya's lips tightened. 'Nothing "goes" between me and Kade Player, and never will!' she answered vehemently, her eyes sparking shoots of green fire. She was practically certain now that Kade had said something.

Lloyd nodded slowly, as if in confirmation. 'I guess I thought as much,' he said quietly. 'So it's Oregon for you, my girl. You're better out of it. There's nothing worse than pipedreams, and I ought to know. Far better to cut loose before they take over.'

This was said in a low bitter voice that Tanya had never heard Lloyd use before, and she sensed that he was referring to the past and to her mother. Where she was concerned, she could not refute his comments. She had lived in a pipedream where Kade was concerned, and the less said about this the better. Perhaps it was just as well that he knew the truth, he would help her to forget. He was not likely ever to refer to it again, of this she was certain.

'So as I said,' went on Lloyd carefully, 'it's better ended. I'm not having you go soft, and doing something you'll regret for the rest of your life.' He squeezed her hand. 'Never look back, Tanya. We're looking to the future from now on. Drink your coffee,' he ordered, 'we've got some shopping to do.'

By the sound of things, Lloyd knew a lot more about the situation than Tanya would have thought possible. By going 'soft' he had meant giving in to Kade's hunting instincts where an attractive woman was concerned. To give the devil his due, this was precisely what Kade was afraid would happen and his pride refused to risk it.

Tanya's eyes misted over. What a champion she had in Lloyd, and what a difference there would have been if her mother had lived, for she would now be free to marry him. She did not consider such thoughts in any way detrimental to her father. It hadn't been fair of him to impose such a stipulation at the time of the separation, even though he had wanted to protect his daughter.

She then remembered Lloyd's bitter comments on pipedreams. Surely he did not regard his love for her mother as a pipedream? It had been very real and very poignant. Looking back to that time, she could now see that her mother had loved Lloyd but was powerless to do anything about it. 'Oh, Lloyd,' she said mistily, 'yours was no pipedream. If it hadn't been for me, Mother would have married you, surely you know that?' she added gently.

Her words stunned Lloyd, who seemed to blanch under his deep tan. 'Say that again,' he said slowly, as if unable to believe his ears.

Tanya could not understand his reaction. It was as if he hadn't known—and if this was so—— 'It was a condition my father imposed upon her,' replied Tanya, still not sure of her ground and very much afraid that she had spoken out of turn.

'You mean that even if she had cared about me, she still couldn't have married me?' he asked in a wondering voice. 'But why couldn't she have told me?' he went on, as he assimilated the news.

There was a time when Tanya might have wondered the same thing, but now she had the answer. 'What good would it have done if she had?' she replied gently. 'You would have hared off to see my father, wouldn't you, and somehow bludgeoned him into releasing her from the contract. She didn't want that, Lloyd. It would have meant her giving up all rights to me.'

There was a long silence after this and she sat anxiously watching Lloyd. Then she saw him open his eyes wide. 'And all this time I thought that she hadn't cared enough to name the date,' he said softly. He looked at Tanya. 'And I thought I was the one going through hell.' He shook his head as if to dispel a mist, then raised Tanya's hand to his lips and gently kissed it. It was a foreign gesture, and one that he did not often make, yet it told Tanya the depth of his feelings. 'You've just made my day, girl,' he said quietly. 'There was so much I couldn't understand. Now I do. I guess she loved me as much as I loved her, and though it's pretty hard to take at this moment, it'll see me through the bad times.'

That was all he said, but it left Tanya in no doubt that she had given him a precious gift, and one that he would treasure for all time. If there was anything worse than losing the one you loved, it was unrequited love. Tanya had already found this to be a very true fact and was only too thankful that she had been able to put the record straight where Lloyd was concerned.

The rest of the morning was spent in goodhumoured argument, with Tanya trying to distract Lloyd from buying various gifts, but she lost out when they passed an elegant-looking jewellers which Lloyd practically dragged her into, and insisted on buying her a delicately engraved gold chain.

It was as if Lloyd had been given a new lease of life, it was in his step, and in his smile, and Tanya found herself wishing that they could just take off for Oregon there and then, thus avoiding the obnoxious task of saying goodbye to Kade and Connie, not to mention the forthcoming discussion with Kade that loomed more menacingly over her as the morning hours slipped away and approached midday.

They returned to the same restaurant for lunch and Tanya found it almost impossible to work up an appetite. Her whole being was centred on what would be her last meeting with Kade, and she only hoped there would be no side issues. She didn't think she could bear it if he adopted the familiar mocking approach that he had so often tormented her with whenever they were alone together. She laid her knife and fork down on her half-finished lobster salad. It was no use, another morsel would choke her.

'Seems we'll have to do something about your appetite,' commented Lloyd, looking at her half-finished meal. 'It used to rival mine, in spite of that sylph-like figure of yours,' he added in mock sorrow, making Tanya respond with a weak grin, but no comment.

Having refused dessert, she was longing to be off. She wanted to get the next hurdle over with as quickly as possible, and, with luck, painlessly.

She was so quiet on the return journey that Lloyd became anxious about her. 'Feeling okay?' he asked her, giving her a quick glance before turning his attention to the road again.

'I was just wondering if I've packed everything,' she lied. 'Most of it's done, and I suppose Connie will remember whatever I've forgotten.'

'I've been thinking of inviting Connie for a visit,' Lloyd said, shrewdly guessing that packing wasn't the only thing on Tanya's mind. 'She told me she'd some relations in Dallas, so she could make it a round trip.'

Tanya gave him a surprised look. 'Has she?' she said. 'She didn't tell me that.'

Lloyd gave a grin at this. 'Well, I guess she was angling for an invite. All she really wants to do is to check up on you. I'm certainly not arguing with those sentiments. Besides,' he added thoughtfully, 'I took to Connie. She's going to be kinda lost now in that big place, isn't she? I think we'll leave it for a few weeks, then invite her over.' He gave Tanya a quick look before he added, 'Then we'll ask her to make the stay permanent. I trust you'll be in favour of such a move?' he asked with a smile.

Tanya gave a quick nod of assent. She hadn't let her thoughts linger on what would happen to Connie after she had gone. She had many friends in the valley, but as Connie herself would have said, they weren't family. It would be nice to have her with her, almost home from home, she thought, and felt a rush of gratitude towards Lloyd for his thoughtfulness.

When they arrived back at Orchard House, Tanya's courage almost deserted her when she saw Kade's sleek

Mercedes drawn up beside the house. At Lloyd's cheerful, 'See you at dinner,' as he started up the Land Rover, she was tempted to ask him to stay and give her moral support, but knew that such a move would infuriate Kade, so she just stood there and watched the tail lights disappear round the bend in the drive.

She found Kade in her father's study, seated at the desk and immersed in paper work. Her heart ached with love for him as she walked slowly towards the desk awaiting an acknowledgement of her arrival. Didn't he care one iota for her? She clenched her hands on the thought. He didn't, and she knew it, but didn't seem able to accept it.

'So you're off tomorrow?' he said abruptly, as if she was going on a cruise, and not right out of his life.

His bright blue stare met her veiled grey-green eyes. Not for worlds would she let him know that he was breaking her heart by his casual approach to what was the end of the line for her.

Kade's eye's travelled down her face slowly and rested on Lloyd's gift, gleaming brightly against the dark blue of her dress. 'Present from Lloyd?' he asked, in a matter-of-fact voice, and before she could answer he went on, 'Seems you're going to be spoilt.'

There was a touch of irony in his voice that did not escape Tanya. 'I still think it would have been better if you'd applied yourself to the task I set you,' he added harshly. 'Work never hurt anyone. It's idleness that causes mischief.'

Tanya's eyes opened wide. Was he accusing her of idleness? 'You didn't give me a chance!' she replied hotly. 'I was quite willing to pull my weight.'

'Were you?' he said scathingly. 'I wonder just how

much you took in about the business during the first few weeks. Very little, unless I miss my guess. It was all a game to you, wasn't it? You'd made your mind up right from the start, hadn't you? In spite of our bargain. And don't tell me I'm wrong,' he shot out at her as she was about to deny this. 'Give me a little credit for some intelligence!'

Tanya sat down weakly on the chair beside the desk. All he had said was true, and there was no point now in denying it. For the first time she saw how it must have been for Kade, who had still tried to keep his end of the bargain. Of the patient lectures he had given her, and the time spent in the offices to give her a good grounding.

She ought to have known she couldn't fool him, and she hadn't really tried to. Half the time she had been so furious with him that she hadn't bothered to hide her indifference.

No wonder he had acted as he had! Taking his revenge on her as compensation for her wilful behaviour. It was small wonder that he hadn't strangled her! She swallowed. In his eyes she still was a child, and a very spoilt one at that. Her attitude had been the same as that of a child determined to have its own way, come what may.

It was a little too late to say that she was sorry now; he wouldn't believe her, and she couldn't blame him. It wouldn't make any difference either way, for now she could see what he had meant when he had said that there was no possibility of them starting afresh. She knew that she would continually annoy him and in doing so, bring out the worst in him. Sooner or later, the inevitable would happen, and this they would both regret.

A cold shiver ran down her back as she envisaged the possible consequences that would follow. Kade would marry her, of that she had no doubt. His sense of honour would ensure this, because she was John Hume's daughter, and only for that reason would he make an honest woman of her. She swallowed. No matter how much she loved him, she didn't want him on those terms.

He had known this, she thought wearily as she looked back at him. He was experienced enough to see the way they were heading. It wouldn't have mattered with anyone else, but not her. Her soft lips firmed; and she had dared to think that he cared for her! All that he had cared about was protecting himself from an embroilment with a young upstart of a girl who happened to bear the name of Hume.

'Isn't it time we got down to business?' she asked quietly, wanting to get it over with in the quickest possible time.

'When I'm good and ready,' growled Kade, and gave her a mocking look. 'In a hurry to be off, are you?' he said jeeringly. 'Looking forward to all those parties your wealthy host is bound to throw in your honour, are you? Well, I haven't finished with you yet. You're not getting off that lightly.'

Tanya stared back at him. Now what? she thought wearily; was he about to deliver a lecture on how she ought to behave once she had cut loose from his restraining hold? Remembering a few of the things she had said at their last meeting, this was not altogether surprising, and she waited for the lecture.

'What kind of a settlement were you hoping for?' he shot out at her.

Tanya blinked. She was taken completely off her guard, and when she had recovered she hated Kade for his insensibility, and for his casual attitude towards her inward misery. 'What do you want me to say?' she replied quietly, wondering how much a broken heart was worth. She couldn't look at him but stared down at her hands twisted together in her lap. 'Only you know what's mine, and what's yours. I only know my share is not very much,' she added on a weary note, 'so you needn't worry about my feeling cheated.'

'For once you're right!' he replied grimly.

Her hands clenched tighter together. She couldn't love him, she thought bewilderedly. He was a brute! Not content with making her fall in love with him he was now twisting the knife in her heart, exacting every ounce of revenge while she was still within reach, and she had to take it, she had no choice. One thing she did know and that was that she'd never let him know how much he had hurt her.

'There's this house, of course,' he went on casually, in a way that invited her comment and made her glance up at him swiftly. 'I'm thinking of moving in,' he added.

Once again his abrupt change of conversation startled her. When he had bought her out he could do what he liked with the property, it was no concern of hers. It would be nice for Connie though, she thought, knowing how much she would welcome such an arrangement. 'Of course,' she murmured politely, showing that she had no objection to such a plan.

Kade's blue eyes pierced through her. 'Is that all you

can say?' he demanded harshly. 'You were born here, remember?'

Tanya swallowed hard. What was she supposed to do? Get down on her knees and plead with him not to send her away? Tell him how much she loved him and that she would do anything he asked of her if only she could stay?

Only the thought of how much he would enjoy watching her squirm prevented her from giving way to these thoughts and throwing caution to the winds. It was just another gambit of his to get his own back on her.

Her resolve hardened when she recalled the way he had accused her of playing a game of pretence when learning the business. He was now indulging in the same kind of game and thoroughly enjoying himself at her expense. 'It's your property now,' she said coldly. 'I didn't think you'd let it remain empty.'

Kade gave her another long searching look that she met with a touch of defiance in hers. The look plainly said, 'You're wasting your time if you're trying to rile me, Kade Player!'

She saw his lips thin, and his strong jaw harden. 'Real little home bird, aren't you?' he said, biting out the words with a viciousness that frightened Tanya. 'I'll get a cheque made out. No doubt you're in a hurry to finish packing,' he added sarcastically, 'so I won't detain you.'

Tanya's mind was in a whirl as she made her way to her room after Kade's abrupt dismissal. She knew she ought to be grateful that she had come out of the meeting relatively unscathed, physically anyway, if not mentally.

Whatever she had imagined would take place at that meeting she had never envisaged it ending with a furious Kade. She shook her head dumbly. It was all wrong, he should have congratulated her on making the right decision, and tried not to smile too heartily as he waved her out of the office and out of his life.

She sat down shakily on the bed. Was it because it hadn't gone exactly as he planned it? He had tried to rile her and he hadn't succeeded, was that why he was so furious?

It was when she recalled something that Connie had said that she thought that she had the answer. Connie had said that she owed Kade a lot for what he'd done for her family. Tanya gulped on the thought. She hadn't said one word of thanks to him, and she ought to have done. If she brought out the worst in Kade, then he had the same effect upon her. When she was with him she couldn't seem to say the right things, only the wrong ones.

They went together like fire and water, she thought sadly, and it wasn't altogether her fault. It was becoming a vicious circle and she was better out of it.

Mechanically, she started finishing her packing. If only things could have been different, she thought miserably, as she closed the case and put it down on the floor beside her other cases. Love was supposed to be a wonderful thing, but it had brought her nothing but misery. When she was away from Kade her heart ached for him, and when she was with him she invariably found herself resenting his highhanded methods.

She heard the slam of the front door and knew that Kade had left the house for his quarters. Her chin came up in a resolute action. She had one last chance to make her peace with him, and she was determined not to be put off this time. There would be an opportunity after dinner, she told herself, for she was certain that Lloyd would take himself off early in order to leave Kade and Tanya to make their final arrangements over the share-out of the business, and if this thought didn't occur to him, then she would ask to see Kade alone.

Tanya made a special point of dressing for dinner that night. She chose her favourite silk dress of ice blue, and knew that it brought out the green lights in her eyes. Her hair came in for special attention too, and she went so far as to touch up her lips with an orange-tinted lipstick that enhanced her honey-coloured tan, that she had still retained even though she had done very little sunbathing since her return to Tasmania.

In her way it was a salute to Kade. She wanted him to remember her this way, even though he saw her as a child, and always would. She put a dab of expensive perfume on her wrist and took one last look in the mirror before going down to join the men, as soon as she heard the one sharp ring of the doorbell that always announced their arrival. Her head was held high as she left the room. She knew that she had achieved her target in making herself look as attractive as possible, and was well satisfied with her appearance.

There was a low 'Wow!' from Lloyd as she entered the dining room, and she waited to hear Kade's comments, glancing swiftly round the room only to find that he was not present.

Her welcoming smile faded as the realisation dawned on her that Kade had chosen to give her a final snub. He wasn't going to be late. He just wasn't coming!

Tanya knew this with painful clarity, even before Lloyd handed her an envelope. 'Kade sent you this,' he said lightly, not realising her inward turmoil as she tried to grasp the fact that Kade could do such a thing to her. 'He sends his apologies,' he went on cheerfully, 'but I guess he's got a heavy date. No doubt he'll be there to see us off tomorrow,' he commented, in a hearty voice that made Tanya want to scream out at him that she wouldn't bet on it. Kade had pushed her out of his life, and in his eyes she had already gone.

CHAPTER ELEVEN

THE following day was a complete blur to Tanya. She knew she had said goodbye to a stern-faced Kade and a weeping Connie standing beside him. She had also politely thanked him for all he had done for her family, and this only served to make Connie's tears flow faster, so she made it quick and to the point.

The next minute they were on their way with Tanya staring straight ahead, not trusting herself to look back and give a last wave.

Lloyd wisely made no comment, but he must have felt like the villain of the piece. Kade's attitude and Connie's tears would have presented such a picture.

Only later, when they were on the plane, did he make a comment on their leavetaking, and then only about Connie. 'She sure took it hard,' he said quietly, and then looked at Tanya who had gone into the numbed state of sheer misery. 'She'll be looking you up in a few months' time. I guess I'll never understand women,' he ended dolefully.

Tanya made a great effort to pull herself out of the doldrums, and told Lloyd that Connie had been with the family for years. 'My going back was like having Mother back again,' she explained gently. 'Connie loved her too, Lloyd.'

At this there was a shadow in his eyes and he nodded slowly, showing her that he understood now, and the rest of the journey was passed in idle comments made at various stages of the trip.

Lloyd's home was all that Tanya had thought it would be, a long low ranch-type building set in acres of surrounding paddocks, with landscaped gardens immediately bordering the home precincts.

If happiness could be bought by luxurious surroundings, then Tanya would have been very happy. She was introduced to the house staff, that consisted of a middle-aged housekeeper who viewed Tanya's youth with a look of consternation in her eyes, but was determined to be polite at all costs, and an elderly man who was introduced as Lloyd's secretary. Then at Lloyd's suggestion, she was taken to her room to freshen up.

The housekeeper who escorted her was pleasant enough but reserved, and it was plain that she had mis-interpreted Tanya's presence in the house, and felt that her employer ought to have known better than to encourage the attentions of a girl young enough to be his daughter.

The room turned out to be a suite, where Tanya had her own bathroom, shower, and sitting room, that could if needs be provide her with a certain amount of privacy. As her travel-weary eyes swept round her domain, she thought of her bedroom at home and it was not a very sensible thing to do, particularly when she recalled that Kade had bought the house from her, and that it was highly unlikely that the long room with its patterned prints of horse motifs, that she had loved and flatly refused to have removed to make way for a modern pattern of wallpaper when the annual decorating was due, would remain as she had known it.

One could not say that the bedroom that she now

stood in bore any resemblance to the room that she was thinking of. Although beautifully furnished, it was somehow impersonal, as all guest rooms were, and brought home the fact that as luxurious as her surroundings were, she did not belong there. She was there for a kind of rehabilitation, she told herself. She had to get Kade out of her system, and she ought to be grateful that there was no time limit on her stay, and that Lloyd actually wanted her there and hoped that she would make the stay permanent.

The days slipped into weeks, and Tanya was swept into a round of social calls that resulted in parties, Lloyd starting them off with a grand affair held especially as a 'how-do party' as Lloyd had put it, to introduce her to his neighbours.

Now that Tanya's position in Lloyd's household was clarified Mrs Jukes, the housekeeper, had lost all of her previous reserve and showed definite signs of wanting to take over Connie's role of half-servant and half-guardian to Tanya.

With so many people willing her to be happy, Tanya felt a traitor in not being able to wholly comply with these sentiments. It was not that she didn't try—she did. She threw herself into the numerous entertainments offered, and rarely an evening went by but either company was expected, or she and Lloyd were due to put in an appearance elsewhere.

This way of life was not new to her, it had been the same when her mother was alive. There had been times in the past when the hectic round of parties, the continual need to be 'having a good time' and a constant wish to 'circulate' and have as many similar minded people around you as possible had mystified Tanya,

who would, had she been given the choice, have settled
for a quieter existence.

She was no longer mystified. With a painful clarity
born out of experience, she now knew why her mother
had acted as she had. She must, she had thought sadly,
have loved Lloyd for a long time, and being the kind
of man he was, he had determinedly set his sights on his
goal, refusing to be put off by her frantic attempts to
remove him from the scene. But that hadn't worked and
the only course left to her was to gather many friends
around her. There was safety in numbers.

These thoughts were going through Tanya's mind as
she dressed for yet another evening out. When she was
ready, she studied her reflection in the long mirror. Her
burnt orange velvet dress clung sleekly to her slim
figure. There was no trace of girlishness now about her,
and it wasn't only the new hair style that she had
adopted, cut very short and shaped close to her head
like a golden cap. It was more than that, she thought,
as she stared at the image before her. It was as if she
had left her youth and dreams back in Tasmania, and
she didn't really know this cool elegant-looking woman
now staring back at her.

With an impatient shrug, she moved away from the
mirror. It must have been Connie's letter that had
brought on this mood of miserable retrospection. It was
always the same after she had received one of her chatty
letters.

It was eight weeks since Tanya had left Orchard
Farm, and during that time she had received four
letters from Connie. Invariably Kade had been mentioned, and considering that he was now living at the
house this was not surprising. She had said that Kade

was quiet—quiet for him, that was, and always seemed to be busy these days, too busy to have the chats they used to have, and she didn't hear much about the business these days.

In her latest letter she had mentioned that Kade was having a wing added to the back of the house, and that she couldn't see why such an extension had been necessary. It was true that Orchard House was not a big house, but surely big enough for his wants?

As she read this Tanya's heart had given a painful leap. What Connie had said about the size of the house was true. Its three bedrooms had been ample for the Humes' small family, but too small for a larger one.

Connie might be mystified about the reasons behind this move of Kade's, but Tanya wasn't. There could only be one reason why Kade should want a larger establishment, and that was marriage. Someone, it appeared, had broken through that protective guard of his and lowered all defences. She must be quite a woman, Tanya thought sadly, only grateful that she was off the scene and would not have to suffer the torment of watching the man she loved pledging his vows to another woman.

In view of this latest development, Connie had had to cancel her visit to Oregon. She couldn't very well be absent when the builders were tramping about the place. They were to start the following week, and as her visit to Tanya was due the week after, she saw no other course but to leave her visit for a later date.

Tanya had not been sorry about this, as she had been secretly dreading Connie's arrival. Connie knew her a little too well to be fooled into believing she was happy. She saw too much, and Tanya couldn't have borne it if she had bluntly said so, for unhappy or not, she had no choice but to make the best of things.

In a way, Tanya thought, as she collected her wrap and left her suite to join Lloyd, it was history repeating itself. Like her mother, she had fallen in love with a man she couldn't have. There was only one little difference, she told herself bitterly. Lloyd had loved her mother, whereas Kade . . .

The murmur of voices floated towards her as she approached the lounge, and her thoughts were still miles away as she entered the room. If they had not been she might have recognised the deep voice of the man standing beside Lloyd by the bar at the end of the room.

Lloyd's hearty, 'Look who's here' made her focus her wide eyes still with that faraway look in them on the tall bronzed figure of the man she had just been thinking of.

Somehow she forced her weak legs to walk forward and held out a polite hand for him to take in greeting, murmuring in a voice she hardly recognised as her own, 'This is a surprise, why didn't you tell us you were coming?'

'It was a snap decision,' replied Kade, his blue stare seeming to engulf her. 'I've just been to a meeting in New York, so I thought I might as well call in while I'm here.' Still keeping his eyes on Tanya, he commented, 'Looks as if I've chosen the wrong evening, you're just about to go off somewhere, aren't you?'

Part of Tanya wanted to hear Lloyd say that they weren't going anywhere special, and of course they could cancel it. That was the part that belonged to her heart. The other part—the level-headed side of her wanted to hear him say that they couldn't very well cancel their plans at this late hour and regretted the fact that they would have to go ahead and keep their appointment.

In the event Lloyd complied with both of her wishes by saying, 'Well, I guess we don't both have to go.' He looked back at the now wary-eyed Tanya. 'We can't both drop out at this hour. I'll leave you to entertain our guest, Tanya. I'll put in an appearance for the Cowleys' dinner, and try to get away early. How's that?' he asked cheerfully.

Tanya tried her best to look grateful, but wasn't sure she succeeded, judging by the familiar mocking look lurking in Kade's eyes. *He knows I don't want to be alone with him,* she thought as her pulse rate increased at the very thought.

There was a little more small talk before Lloyd left them, charging Tanya with the task of keeping Kade's glass filled, and showing him the garden of which he was justly proud. 'I take it you're staying the night?' he asked Kade, before he left, and to Tanya's further consternation Kade had given a confirming nod and drawled, 'Several, if convenient.'

Lloyd was pleased about this if Tanya wasn't, and gave an approving nod. 'In that case, I needn't rush back,' he answered with a grin.

During the silence that followed Lloyd's departure, Tanya wondered if Kade could hear her thudding heartbeats, and when he quickly finished his whisky she almost rushed to refill his glass. Her nervous hand never reached the bottle as Kade's strong one closed over it. 'Later, Tanya. I want to talk to you,' he said softly.

Tanya snatched her hand away from the contact that

had sent her pulse rate soaring. It was so easy for him, she thought bitterly. Everything was going his way. Was it falling in love that had made him see how shabbily he had treated her? Did he want to make sure that she was happy? If she had been beaten twice a day by Lloyd, she wouldn't have told him!

She remembered the cheque that she had never thanked him for. It was a much larger sum than she was entitled to, even with the house included, but somehow she had never been able to write and thank him. 'Thank you for your cheque,' she said stiffly, quite unable to meet his eyes. 'It was more than I should have had,' she ended lamely.

'Blast the cheque!' exploded Kade savagely. 'I didn't come to talk about that.'

Tanya's lovely grey-green eyes met his squarely. 'What did you come for, Kade? To see how I'm faring?' She moved away from him, her slim back straight, and did a little pirouette as she turned to face him. 'I'm very well, as you can see,' she said lightly. 'Now what else can we talk about? Or shall I show you the garden? It really is worth seeing,' she added, on a rising note of panic as she saw Kade stride purposefully towards her. 'I'm not in your territory now, Kade Player,' she said, as she backed towards the door. 'This is Lloyd's house.'

She might have known she wouldn't be allowed to reach the door, and found herself jerked into Kade's arms with a force that knocked the breath out of her. 'Leading with your chin, as usual,' he said grimly, as he put a hard hand under her chin making her look up at him.

The bliss of finding herself in those strong arms of his once more was marred by what had gone before, and her interpretation of the news in Connie's letter. Was this a last fling of his before he committed himself to one woman? Whoever she was, she would never hear of it; she was miles away and Kade was safe from onlookers.

Why must he always pick on her? she thought wildly, as she struggled to free herself. Why couldn't he pick on someone else for a change? 'Taking a last bite at forbidden fruit?' she asked him bitterly, when she realised that he was not going to let her go.

'Who said it was forbidden?' Kade asked softly, his eyes on her soft lips.

'You did,' said Tanya breathlessly, making another futile bid for freedom because she knew that he was going to kiss her.

There was a hint of mockery in his blue eyes as his lips neared hers. 'Seeing how scratched I got in collecting that fruit I think I deserve it,' he murmured, before his lips met hers.

Kade had kissed her before, but not like this. At first it was gentle and reassuring, featherlight and teasing to the senses, then it took on an entirely different meaning. It was possessive, yet persuasive, and it melted Tanya's bones to jelly.

When his lips left hers, she was completely drained of all opposition to his wishes. She knew a deep fear, a helplessness that she had never known before. Her wide pleading eyes gazed into his hooded ones. 'Give me a chance, Kade,' she whispered, in an agonised voice. If he kissed her like that again then she would be lost, and she was asking him not to and to leave her alone to try and make the best out of what little happiness she would have left when he had gone.

'I gave you a chance,' he said gruffly, 'and it cost me too much. I can't afford to give you another one. You're coming back with me, my girl, and this time we'll do things right.'

Tanya's muddled senses could make no headway of this at all. What did he mean? Was he talking about the cheque he had given her? 'You can have it back, Kade,' she said, taking the opportunity of slipping out of range of his arms. 'I've still got it.'

Kade's lips thinned at this. 'I guess we're still at cross-purposes,' he said quietly, and before Tanya could move, he had her back in his arms again. 'I said you're coming back with me. You can keep the cheque as a wedding present. Buy yourself one of those white trailing dresses with orange blossom on it, or whatever you fancy wearing at our wedding. Just as long as you say the right words at the right time for a change, I don't much care,' he ordered autocratically, 'but I ought to warn you, it's going to be a big occasion.'

Tanya could only stare at him. 'Our wedding,' he had said. She still couldn't believe it. He hadn't asked her to marry him, and surely he ought to have done? Her heart skipped a beat as the thought occurred to her that he might just have wanted her to be present at his wedding. She swallowed. 'Would you mind being a little more explicit?' she asked in a small voice.

Kade's answer was given in a typically Kade-like way, and she was left in no doubt of what he had in mind.

As he told her in a slightly gruff voice a little later, 'At this rate you won't be wearing white. I don't think we're going to have time to wait to hear the banns read!'

A little while later they strolled in Lloyd's flower-scented gardens, and Tanya felt as if she were dreaming, only the hard reassuring pressure of Kade's hand in hers told her that it wasn't a dream and was actually happening. 'Did you miss me very much?' she asked, in a low half-teasing voice, wanting yet again to hear that he loved her. 'Why didn't you come sooner? I've had eight weeks of misery,' she accused him gently.

'Because I promised Lloyd,' was Kade's quiet reply.

Tanya glanced up at him; she could just discern his strong features in the gathering dusk. 'Promised Lloyd?' she repeated. 'What did you promise Lloyd?' she asked curiously.

'That I'd leave you alone for a couple of months,' Kade answered. 'He knew I was crazy about you, and he didn't want you pushed into anything until you were sure of your own mind.'

He was silent for a few moments before he added, 'There was the question of age, too. I guess he felt much as I did about that. I'd intended to let you go anyway. Remember what you said about not making the mistake of falling for an older man?' he reminded her, rather cruelly Tanya thought, but she forgave him. 'Then you declared an interest in the antiquated species, due, you said, to my enlightenment,' he added teasingly. 'It didn't leave me much of an excuse for not going ahead and claiming what I felt was mine.'

His arm crept round her waist and he pulled her close to him. 'I warned Lloyd then that he might be travelling alone.' His grip on her tightened, but Tanya didn't mind the discomfort. 'But his objections were so near my previous thoughts on the matter that I knew he was right. In a sense I wasn't giving you a chance. I knew that you were as attracted to me as I was to you, but I was old enough to know the real thing when it happened. You weren't, and it would have been my bad luck if it had only been a passing attraction on your part. Either way, I had to give you that chance.'

'Is that why you didn't come to my farewell dinner?' Tanya asked, caressing his strong jaw with a loving finger, and remembering the desolation she had felt at his absence.

Kade caught her hand and kissed it. 'It was hard enough letting you go,' he said softly, 'but sitting opposite you at the dinner table and realising that I was probably going to lose you for good was more than I could take. Besides,' his lips touched the golden crown of her head, 'I couldn't trust myself to adhere to my good intentions. I tried to rile you into a tantrum in the study, if you remember. I wanted a chance to hold you in my arms again, and if that had happened——' he gave a casual shrug, 'you wouldn't have left with Lloyd the following day.'

He kissed her gently. 'If you've been miserable these past few weeks, imagine what I felt like, knowing that my golden girl was dancing the night hours away in someone else's arms.' His arms tightened around her, enclosing her in an action that was both protective and possessive. 'Don't grow up too fast, my darling,' he whispered against her hair. 'I love you just the way you are.'

You didn't grow old, Tanya thought mistily, not deep inside you when you had everything to live for as she had, and as her lips met his she thought of Orchard House and the extensions he had had put in hand. He had not intended to accept a refusal from her, and she ought to have been slightly shocked at his ruthless determination to achieve his goal. Instead, she felt immensely proud that such a man should love her.

The **HARLEQUIN CLASSIC LIBRARY**
is offering some of the best in romance
fiction—great old classics from our early
publishing lists.

On the following page is a coupon with which
you may order any or all of these titles. If you
order all nine, you will receive a free book—*Meet
the Warrens*, a heartwarming classic romance by
Lucy Agnes Hancock.

The first nine novels in the

HARLEQUIN
CLASSIC LIBRARY

1 Do Something Dangerous Elizabeth Hoy
2 Queen's Counsel Alex Stuart
3 On the Air Mary Burchell
4 Doctor Memsahib Juliet Shore
5 Castle in Corsica Anne Weale
6 So Dear to My Heart Susan Barrie
7 Cameron of Gare Jean S. MacLeod
8 Doctor Sara Comes Home Elizabeth Houghton
9 Summer Lightning Jill Tahourdin

Great old favorites...
Harlequin Classic Library

Complete and mail this coupon today!

Harlequin Reader Service

In U.S.A.
MPO Box 707
Niagara Falls, N.Y. 14302

In Canada
649 Ontario St.
Stratford, Ontario, N5A 6W2

Please send me the following novels from the Harlequin Classic Library.
I am enclosing my check or money order for $1.25 for each novel ordered,
plus 59¢ to cover postage and handling. If I order all nine titles, I will receive
a free book, *Meet the Warrens*, by Lucy Agnes Hancock.

☐ 1   ☐ 4   ☐ 7
☐ 2   ☐ 5   ☐ 8
☐ 3   ☐ 6   ☐ 9

Number of novels checked @ $1.25 each =	$ _____
N.Y. State residents add appropriate sales tax	$ _____
Postage and handling	$ _____ .59
TOTAL	$ _____

I enclose _____
(Please send check or money order. We cannot be responsible for cash sent
through the mail.)
Prices subject to change without notice.

Name _____
(Please Print)

Address _____

City _____

State/Prov. _____

Zip/Postal Code _____